BUSINESS AND PROJECT MANAGEMENT FOR CONTRACTORS

MARYLAND HOME IMPROVEMENT COMMISSION EDITION

Fourth Edition

National Association of State
Contractors Licensing Agencies
Post Office Box 14941
Scottsdale, Arizona 85267

Business and Project Management for Contractors — Maryland Home Improvement
Commission Edition, Fourth Edition
First Printing   October 2004
Second Printing   February 2005

Copyright © 2001, 2002, 2003, and 2004 by the
National Association of State
Contractors Licensing Agencies
NASCLA
P.O. Box 14941
Scottsdale, Arizona 85267

Published by
NASCLA Publications, Inc.

The information contained in this directory is being provided as a service to the construction industry. Although the information contained herein is believed to be correct at the time of printing, changes in laws and regulations occur regularly. It is the contractors' responsibility to review their activities with their attorneys, accountants, and tax professionals. The publishers do not assume, and hereby disclaim, any liability to any party for loss or damage caused by any errors or omissions in this publication.

This publication is designed to provide accurate and authoritative information in a highly summarized manner with regard to the subject matter covered. It is sold with the understanding that the publisher is not engaged in rendering legal, technical, or other professional service. If legal and other expert assistance is required, the services of competent professionals should be sought.

Authors

Herschel C. Adcock, Sr., J.D.
Lauren Daniels
Michael D. Hay
Jerry Householder, Ph.D.
Stephen P. Schmidt, CPA
Stephen A. Vitali, M.A., M.B.A.

ISBN 1-889834-62-9

FOREWORD

The National Association of State Contractors Licensing Agencies (NASCLA) was formed in 1962, as a not for profit organization. The association is composed of states that have enacted laws to regulate the business of contracting. It is dedicated to the mutual assistance of the member states in striving for better regulation of the construction industry to protect the health, safety, and welfare of the general public.

In 1990, the NASCLA Board of Directors voted to develop a national contractors business management guide. This decision was due, in large part, to the fact that over 85% of contractor failures result from business reasons, not from lack of trade knowledge. In 1997 alone, there were 10,867 construction company failures, listing over $2,021,000,000 in liabilities! Over one-third of these firms were less than five years old. These numbers do not include the many contractors that, without formal court action, decided for various reasons to discontinue operations.

The construction industry in this country is one of the largest single contributors to the national economy. Despite its size, the industry is made up mostly of small businesses (over 800,000). To a small construction firm, the business world can be a dangerous place; everything may seem stacked against the success of the company. Among other factors, government regulations, squeezed cash flows, tightened profit margins, and a lack of skilled labor have given the construction industry one of the highest failure rates of any trade.

Because the construction business is easy to get into, many people enter the construction field without sufficient business management skills. The small contractor can no longer be just a craftsman; today, more is required. Now, in order to survive, the contractor must be a total business manager.

The NASCLA Board of Directors felt that the use of a common guide would not only help provide a basic understanding of business management subjects to license applicants, but also could promote the standardization of licensing examinations, aid in reciprocity agreements among the states, and reduce the reference materials required of license exam candidates.

The Maryland *Business and Project Management for Contractors* is designed to provide an overview of business management subjects for contractor examination candidates. It is also written to act as a reference guide for licensed contractors.

The guide is divided into two major sections. *Part One* deals with business and project management subjects relevant to contractors everywhere. *Part Two* focuses on the unique home improvement contracting requirements of Maryland.

In *Part One,* the nine chapters provide an introduction to the following subjects:

◊ *Planning and Organizing*—describes the various forms a business may take, establishing a business, and preparing a business plan.

◊ *Risk Management*—covers the risks associated with contracting and the types of insurance policies and bonding used to protect the contractor and customer.

◊ *Ethics in Construction*—explains the standards of conduct when dealing with others.

◊ *Estimating*—covers bidding, the estimating process, and methods for estimating materials, labor, equipment, and overhead.

◊ *Scheduling*—shows the planning, scheduling, cash flow, and control processes necessary for a complex project.

◊ *Environmental and Safety Considerations*—covers the job site environmental issues and safety, as well as asbestos and lead abatement issues.

◊ *Employer Obligations*—explores the various federal acts that control the hiring, paying, and related labor issues associated with employees.

◊ *Financial Management*—covers the accounting process and methods, as well as financial statements, ratios, and job costing.

◊ *Contract* Law—goes through the aspects of entering into a contract and contract terminology.

In *Part Two,* the six chapters explain the unique issues involved in home improvement construction contracting in Maryland. These chapters include the following:

◊ *Doing Business in Maryland*—lists and explains the function of various state agencies that impact the business operation of a contractor in the state.

◊ *Home Improvement Contractor Licensing in Maryland*—summarizes the licensing requirements of the Home Improvement Commission.

◊ *State Labor Laws*—includes worker's compensation and unemployment insurance, as well as wage and hour laws.

◊ *Business Taxes and Reporting Requirements*—covers income taxes, business license fees, payroll taxes, and sales tax.

◊ *Maryland Safety*—summarizes the safety requirements added by the Maryland Occupational and Safety Act to the federal requirements.

◊ *Lien Law*—explains the unique features and notice requirements of contractor liens.

The *Appendices* at the end of the guide provide the full text of the statutes and rules that control the major activities of contracting in Maryland, as well as other relevant federal and state references.

TABLE OF CONTENTS

Chapter 4 continued…..

Chapter 5   Scheduling

Chapter 6   Environmental & Safety Considerations

Chapter 6 continued....

Chapter 7   Employer Obligations

Chapter 8   Financial Management

Chapter 9   Contract Law

PART TWO – STATE REQUIREMENTS FOR MARYLAND HOME IMPROVEMENTS

CHAPTER 1
PLANNING AND ORGANIZING

DO I WANT MY OWN BUSINESS?

The prospect of owning and operating a business is an exciting one, to say the least. Among the many advantages are:

◊ Being your own boss; no one can fire you.

◊ Having full control of work schedules and a choice of customers.

◊ Working results in an investment in your business, not just a paycheck.

◊ There is no limit to what can be earned.

This sounds almost too good to be true. In fact, it is true, and those who own and operate their own businesses have known this for years. However, business owners are also aware of the disadvantages of being an owner. Some of the disadvantages are:

◊ Payroll must be met each week and you are fully responsible for the business.

◊ Work hours will be longer than your employees' work hours and quitting is much more complicated than just handing in a resignation.

◊ Responding to bad business conditions will require sharp business skills.

◊ Government regulations will add cost to services and will be one of the major drivers of the business.

◊ Customers, creditors, competition, and economic forces, over which you have no control, will be major factors in the success of the business.

Despite these disadvantages, independent businesses succeed mainly because of careful planning and implementation.

As part of planning for a successful business, the following questions require careful consideration:

◊ What financial resources do I need to start a business? Consider costs related to equipment, rental of office space, and support of personal living expenses until an income is generated, as well as initial start-up costs like licensing and attorney's fees.

◊ What are my skills? Consider your skills and the type of contracting business for which they are best suited: remodeling and home improvement, custom building, general engineering, or a subcontracting specialty.

◊ How much building activity is going on in my location? Consider past and present building activity and research local trends. Pay special attention to the forecast of the local economy.

◊ How much risk can I afford to take? Consider how much you can afford to lose due to the variable costs of materials and services; delays caused by weather, regulations, or customers; and the ability to employ qualified personnel.

◊ What will I do about record keeping? Consider whether to handle these matters yourself or if support staff, such as a bookkeeper, office manager, or secretary, will be needed.

These are not easy questions to answer. However, before starting a business, these are questions that need to be answered as completely as possible. The complexity of the marketplace, the failure rate of small business, and federal, state, and local regulations require careful planning and organization. The days of throwing tools in the old pick-up and calling yourself a contractor are long gone.

CHOOSING THE FORM OF YOUR BUSINESS

Now that a decision has been made to start a contracting business, one of the first things to do is determine what form the business will take. By form, we are referring to the legal form of the business, which will determine how the business, and perhaps the owners, will be taxed; the extent of personal liability; how the business will be funded; and who will be in control of the business.

As of this writing, there are at least eight different legal forms a business can take. New forms of business always seem to be in development in response to market needs and the general economic condition of the country.

Our discussion of business entities will focus on the four most common forms of business organization. We will also briefly note others that are more complex, but may be appropriate for a specific business purpose. Consideration of the latter forms of business should be done in consultation with a tax accountant and an attorney.

The four basic forms of business organization are:

1. Sole Proprietorship
2. Partnership
3. Corporation
4. S Corporation

Sole Proprietorship (Sole Ownership)

The sole proprietorship (or individual) is essentially the simplest form of doing business. In essence, the business and the owner are totally connected; there is no separation of the owner and the business in terms of funding, liability, taxation, or control.

The *advantages* of a sole proprietorship are:

◊ It is easy to establish and terminate.

◊ The owner is in total control of the business.

◊ The business, or any part of it, can be sold, altered, or exchanged at will.

With the ease and simplicity of a sole proprietorship come several *disadvantages*:

◊ Creditors may seize personal as well as business property in settlement of business debts.

◊ Personal liability for debt and negligence is unlimited.

◊ The business relies primarily on the sole owner's financial resources.

◊ The business does not survive the death or departure of the owner.

◊ There is little if any tax advantage.

Partnership

A partnership may be limited (discussed later) or general. A general partnership is a legal relationship in which two or more persons are contractually associated as principals in a business. Because all partners are individually liable for the debts and obligations of the partnership, it is essential that a written agreement be drawn up to specify the rights and responsibilities of the partners, especially as related to control of the business and the sharing of profits and losses.

Partnerships have several *advantages*. They provide the owners with the opportunity to:

◊ share financial resources;

◊ share knowledge and skill in running the business; and

◊ share the risk of operating the business.

Although it would appear that partnerships limit liability, they do not. In fact, in this regard the *disadvantages* of a partnership are the same as those for a sole proprietorship. The partners are totally liable for all debts of the partnership. Should any of the partners fail to meet their obligations, the other partners can be forced to pay.

It is this unlimited liability for debt that dictates the need for a formal agreement between the partners to specify the individual limits of liability.

Corporation

Corporations are legal entities formed under the laws of the state in which they are created. Corporations conduct business as a legal person and can enter into contracts, pay taxes, hire staff, file lawsuits, borrow money, and raise money by issuing stock.

The *advantages* of corporations include:

◊ limited liability for the debts and actions of the corporation; while the officers may have some personal liability for the actions of the corporation, the stockholders generally do not;

◊ continuous life; the corporation does not end with the death or withdrawal of the principal owners, as is the case in a sole proprietorship or partnership; and

◊ transfer of ownership without hindrance (unless specifically limited in the articles of incorporation).

While corporations have several advantages over partnerships and sole proprietorships, they do have some *disadvantages*:

◊ They are generally the most costly to organize.

◊ State and federal regulation of corporations can be excessive.

◊ Record keeping usually requires professional help.

◊ Income generated by the corporation is taxed at the corporate rate and then taxed again when the stockholders report their dividends.

S Corporation

One specialized type of corporation, the "S" Corporation, deserves mention as a potential form for business. This entity has all the benefits of a corporation, plus a different method of taxation. An S Corporation pays no income tax on most of its revenues. Instead, the shareholders elect to report the corporate income or loss on their individual tax returns. As a result, double taxation is avoided. However, if this form of organization is selected, adherence to some very strict rules set forth by the Internal Revenue Service is required. We recommend consultation with an attorney or tax advisor before forming an S Corporation.

Other Forms of Organization

Earlier in this section, we noted that there were at least eight different forms of organization for businesses. We have described four of them. Next, we will briefly describe some other business forms for consideration. Again, because of their unique natures, discussion about these forms with an attorney and tax advisor is strongly recommended.

Joint Ventures

Joint ventures are customarily reserved for those situations in which two or more entities want to join together on a special project. This is usually limited to a single transaction; typically, joint ventures are not used to conduct business on an ongoing basis.

Joint ventures have essentially the same advantages and disadvantages of partnerships. It is strongly recommended that joint venture arrangements be made in writing. Because joint ventures are time limited, the agreement should include a clear description of not only how business will be conducted, but also when it will end.

Limited Partnerships

Limited partnerships are usually arrangements for a single project or type of project. Persons wanting to invest in and benefit from the workings of a partnership, without the liability that is associated with the operation of the partnership, provide funds to general partners for the operation of the business. The limited partner's risk for financial loss is limited to his or her investment. The number of percentage of shares of the partnership that he or she holds also limits his chance for profit. Limited partners may not take an active role in the day-to-day operations of the business.

Limited Liability Companies

Limited liability companies are very similar to partnerships and are treated as sole proprietorships, partnerships or corporations for the reporting of income and the payment of taxes. Their primary benefits are:

◊ Regulations covering formation and operation are generally easier.

◊ The members are protected against the company's liability for debt and negligence.

◊ A simpler and more informal decision making process than the corporate form.

◊ Greater flexibility in allocating profits and losses than the corporate form.

◊ Easier owner dispute resolution process.

It is important to obtain qualified legal advice in the forming of a limited liability company (LLC), as requirements may vary from state to state, for example, not all states allow one person LLCs.

Business Trusts

Business trusts may be treated as either corporations or partnerships, depending on the individual company's structure. Business trusts are created, generally, to hold or protect property for beneficiaries.

THE BUSINESS PLAN

Perhaps the single most important thing to help ensure success of the business is the preparation of a business plan. Without a business plan, the chance of becoming a successful operation is significantly reduced. Very few of us are lucky enough to find that one opportunity that, by its very nature, commands the attention and respect of customers. Even fewer of us can keep all the details of markets, products, and services organized in our heads in such a way that we can readily translate those thoughts into actions.

A business plan need not be a bound document; it can be written on the office walls. It does not have to be typed; it can be handwritten in crayon. It cannot and should not be a "static", fixed document. It needs to be "alive" and changing with the changing marketplace.

Above all, the business plan is *your* plan and it must reflect *your* thinking about what you do best and how you do it. Certainly, the counsel and guidance of legal and tax advisors, family members, friends, and associates are helpful, but in the final analysis, the plan is *yours*. You have to own it and you have to execute it.

There are several formats for a business plan. Most are available in books on the subject or via inexpensive computer software. Business plans follow a rather similar format, leaving it up to you to determine how simple or complex the plan will be. In general, the more complete the plan; the more likely it will be used to meet the business objectives.

The following section provides a general outline of a business plan, with each area defined.

Summary

This is the section that identifies the business, including its owner(s), location, and general purpose. In this section, include some of the major highlights of your plan.

Description

This section includes a brief account of the background, including skills and expertise of the owner(s). This section also includes an in-depth description of the services that are being offered.

Markets

This section must focus on the opportunity for the business in the locale chosen. To complete this section, extensive research of the current needs in the selected market and the strengths of competitors is required.

Marketing Strategy

Who are your customers? What specific steps will be taken to market (sell) and deliver your service?

Operating Considerations

In this section, answer these questions:

◊ Who is the work force?

◊ What facilities will be used?

◊ What are the capital requirements?

◊ How will quality control be implemented?

◊ Where will you obtain the financial resources?

◊ How will services be evaluated?

Management

Discuss how the business will be managed, who the employees will be, and what experience will be needed to make the business a success.

Finances

Prepare a budget based on a forecast of how much business can be generated, how services will be priced, and the break-even point of the business. Be *honest* and *conservative*.

Other

Prepare a forecast of where the business will be in three to five years; consider how the business will be developed. A business plan is not only an essential element of the start-up, but it can also be used to seek additional capital or convince others to join the venture. Therefore, make sure the plan is as complete as possible and make it, above all, an honest assessment. This is not the time for unrealistic or overly optimistic numbers.

ESTABLISHING A BUSINESS

Before deciding on the form of organization for the business, consider the following:

◊ financial resources and sources of support for the venture;

◊ personal liability limitations;

◊ risk tolerance;

◊ desired level of control of the business;

◊ state and federal regulations governing the form of business;

◊ specific construction business skills that you have;

◊ outside services required; and

◊ the scope of the business.

This sounds like a lot of work before even a single nail has been driven, and it is. However, it is important to remember that today's success is the result of yesterday's preparation.

Once a decision has been made regarding the form of business, it is then time to perform a series of tasks that will *allow* you to conduct business.

Notice that we say, *"allow"* rather than saying *"can"*. This distinction is important and again refers to the planning process for entering a business. Each step taken is part of the plan to consider if and how you will do business.

The next step is to identify the things to be done before you can ply your trade. In order to be allowed to do business in most states certain steps, described below, must be taken.

◊ Obtain a contractor's license. This is required regardless of the form of the business. *Some states can file criminal charges against persons contracting without a license.*

◊ Obtain local licenses, as required. Many counties and municipalities have their own licensing requirements.

◊ Register any fictitious names. Business names, unless it is your own and unless you are a sole proprietorship, should be registered to protect them. In some cases, business names must be registered to provide a public record of the person(s) behind the business.

◊ Prepare and file Articles of Incorporation. This is required for the corporate form of organization.

◊ Prepare partnership agreements. Obviously, this is necessary only if the business is organized as a partnership or limited partnership.

◊ Obtain a federal employer identification number (EIN). This is required for all forms of organizations, except for sole proprietorships that do not have employees (in those cases, the owner's social security number may be used). The EIN is unique to a business entity and may not be transferred to another entity, regardless of ownership. Form SS-4 is used to apply for an EIN.

◊ Acquire workers' compensation insurance, if there are employees.

◊ Obtain liability insurance to protect the assets of the business.

◊ Obtain other types of specialty insurance, such as bonds, builders risk, vehicle coverage, installation floaters, or other forms of coverage, as required. While these may be considered essential, most do not have to be secured until just before work, related to the business, is actually performed.

MANAGING A BUSINESS

Regardless of the form of the organization, it has to be managed. Sole proprietors, partners, associates, or professional managers can manage businesses.

Managers are responsible for a broad range of duties, including hiring and firing employees, overseeing day-to-day operations and ensuring that customer needs are met. Whether or not to hire a professional manager is a question that requires consideration of the owner's management skills, the scope and size of the business, whether or not the owner(s) will be performing the actual construction work in addition to managing those who do, and, frankly, what is affordable.

Whether a manager is hired, or managerial duties are performed by an owner, an assessment of the effectiveness of the management of the business is required. Some of the questions relating to an assessment of a manager would be:

◊ Is the manager knowledgeable about the type of business being conducted?

◊ Does the manager have the ability to identify business opportunities for growth?

◊ Does the manager take appropriate risks in expanding the business?

◊ Does the manager focus on customer needs?

◊ Does he or she have a systematic way to measure customer satisfaction?

◊ Is the manager a team player, understanding management's role on the team—accepting responsibility for team results, good or bad?

◊ Does the manager communicate clearly, verbally and in writing, with employees and customers?

◊ Is the manager an effective problem solver? Can he or she spot problems before they occur and then act to develop acceptable alternatives and solutions?

◊ Does the manager organize the business process and work deadlines so that important dates are not missed and customers' time needs are met?

◊   Does the manager control the cost of doing business without sacrificing quality or compromising safety or industry standards?

◊   Does the manager stay current with industry advancements?

◊   Does the manager hire and retain qualified staff?

Those are some of the basic questions that must be answered when considering anyone for the manager's role. They can be looked at as a qualification list for managers and can be used to develop a set of interview questions and a method of evaluation of the managers' skills.

CHAPTER 2
RISK MANAGEMENT

Contracting is a risky business. You are always faced with the threats of loss, damage, and injury—dangers that can destroy your business. Typical examples of these dangers are fire, theft, accidental injury of employees and customers, and loss of key employees. These unexpected occurrences are called risks. You must identify the risks that your business faces in order to determine the best way to protect it from those risks. Your goal should be to eliminate, minimize, shift, or absorb any losses you suffer because of these unanticipated risks. Contractors are obligated to protect their employees and customers, and in some cases are required to do so by law. Furthermore, contractors must protect themselves against unavoidable disasters.

CONTRACTING RISKS

Successful contractors understand that the responsibility for potential liability created by the acts of others should be shifted from themselves to the other party, if possible. This might be done by contract. For example, when you are negotiating a job, you should require the subcontractor to agree in a written contract to indemnify you, hold you harmless, and provide your legal defense in the event of an accident involving the subcontractor's work. Indemnify means to pay you for whatever you have to pay someone else. Remember that since most insurance contracts require the policyholder to pay a deductible, you may want to shift that responsibility in the contract. Further, you might wish to require in the contract that the subcontractor add your business as an additional insured under his or her policy.

Before entering into a contract with another party or a subcontractor, ask to see his or her certificates of insurance for each type of coverage required and then call his or her insurance agent to confirm that coverage. Before a contract is signed, you should request that your attorney and/or insurance agent review the contract to determine your exposure to risks and the adequacy of coverage in place.

INSURANCE

Insurance is a contractor's protection against risk. If a profitable business does not have enough insurance, it can be wiped out overnight by a single natural disaster or major accident.

An insurance policy is a contract in which the insurer promises to pay for a specific loss or liability, if it occurs. The specific losses and liabilities covered depend on the type of insurance (different types of insurance are discussed below). Because of its relationship to the public welfare, the insurance business is controlled and regulated by federal and state laws. If a contractor suffers a loss due to his or her own deliberate action, the loss is not covered by insurance.

Construction contracts often require the contractor to obtain certain types of insurance coverage, such as workers' compensation (employment liability) and comprehensive liability insurance.

Contracts may also require the contractor to indemnify, or hold harmless, the owner and the architect by accepting any liability that they incur under the contract. It is good practice for a contractor to submit a copy of the contract document to his or her insurance agency, as well as his or her lawyer, before signing the contract and beginning construction.

Contractors can generally find policies to protect them against most types of risks. You will at least want to obtain motor vehicle, general liability, and workers' compensation insurance. You also might want to purchase umbrella coverage for added protection, depending on the size of your business and the risks you face. Umbrella policies extend the limits of your coverage.

INSURANCE AGENTS

An agent is the person who sells the insurance to you. He or she sells coverage either directly for the insurance carrier he or she represents, or as a broker who may represent several carriers. The insurance needs of each business are unique. Ask the agent if he or she has experience in your field and ask for his or her references. Call the Department of Insurance to see if any complaints have been lodged against the agent. Make sure your agent places coverage only with carriers who are admitted in your state to transact business, have been rated "A" or better, and have experience in your business. You should also meet with the agent and ask him or her what kind of support you will receive. Is he or she willing and able to review your contracts to see if your coverage is sufficient?

TYPES OF POLICIES

Next, we will discuss some of the more common types of insurance carried by contractors.

Workers' Compensation

Workers' compensation insurance protects employers from liability for injuries to employees on the job. State and sometimes federal laws require the employer to maintain this type of insurance coverage for employees. The coverage includes medical expenses, rehabilitation, partial payment of wages, and other benefits.

Automobile (Motor Vehicle) Insurance

Motor vehicle insurance protects your business against property damage and personal injury claims arising out of the use, operation, or maintenance of your company's vehicles.

Property Insurance

Property insurance protects your business and personal property against loss due to fire, theft, vandalism, and weather-related incidents.

Comprehensive General Liability (CGL)

Comprehensive General Liability insurance (CGL) protects your company against claims for bodily injury to people who are not employees of your company. CGL also protects against claims for damage to property belonging to someone other than your company. CGLs can protect the contractor when accidents happen either on the premises or away from the premises during business operations.

Your basic CGL policy will state that it covers money payments that you, the insured contractor, become legally obligated to pay because of bodily injury or property damage to others.

There are two types of coverage that are typically included in a standard CGL policy. They are premises-operations hazards and products completed operations hazards. Premises-operations hazard insurance covers accidents that arise out of:

◊   the condition of the contractor's premises, or

◊   the contractor's operations in progress.

If you manufacture, re-manufacture, sell, or resell goods, you should have products completed operations hazard coverage. It covers defective products when they are out of your hands or completed work away from your premises. If you install or build things away from your premises, you may want to get this type of coverage.

Your policy will limit coverage to accidents that occur during the policy period. Only accidents are covered; the injury or damage cannot be intentional, planned, or expected. If the person or the property is not actually injured or damaged until after the policy expires, you are probably not covered.

For example, a welding company had an "occurrence-based" policy in effect when it made a weld on a boom crane. The policy provided completed operations coverage. However, later, after that policy expired, the boom broke due to the defective welding job and it damaged someone's property. The court said that, even though the accident was a result of the defective welding job, the accident that resulted in damages occurred after the policy expired. Therefore, coverage was denied.

This raises the question, "What is an occurrence?" A boom crane falling on property is obviously an occurrence. However, the definition becomes more ambiguous when, for example, an injury does not show itself for a long time. This is often seen in asbestos-related illnesses and pollution-related cancer. Some courts approach such cases by saying that an occurrence happens when the person is exposed to harmful conditions, even if that person's illness does not become evident until years later.

Your CGL policy will typically provide a maximum coverage limit for each occurrence. This can be complicated. If you have an accident on a job that damages all the homes on one city block, is each house an occurrence, or do they all constitute one occurrence? Some courts would hold that each person's house was damaged by a separate occurrence; therefore, the insurance company would be obligated to pay up to the limits of coverage to each person whose house was damaged.

CGL Exclusions

Most CGL policies contain several standard exclusions. Exclusions are activities or certain types of property that will not be covered by the policy. You may want to pay extra to remove one or more of the exclusions, or you can purchase separate coverage for them, depending on your individual needs. The more common exclusions are listed below.

Work Product

Your CGL policy does not insure the quality of your products or your work. If, for example, you build homes and there are defects in the construction, the policy will not pay to correct those defects.

Warranties

Like the work product exclusion, the CGL policy will not cover a breach of any warranties you may have given covering the quality of your work product or the actual manner in which your work was done.

Automobiles (Motor Vehicles)	Most CGL policies exclude bodily injury or property damage arising out of the operation, use, loading, or unloading of your motor vehicle or aircraft. You should obtain a separate motor vehicle insurance policy to cover those risks. However, the policies commonly do not include "mobile equipment" in the definition of motor vehicle. This means mobile equipment is covered under most CGL policies. Generally speaking, "mobile equipment" includes land vehicles that you use on your job that are designed for use off of public roads. This includes equipment like cranes, rollers, concrete mixers, welding equipment, and the like. Some contractors might have specialized equipment that is moved from job to job. It is wise to obtain separate coverage, a floater, to cover this type of equipment wherever it is located.
Watercraft	Damage arising out of the operation, use, loading, or unloading of watercraft will ordinarily not be covered by your CGL policy.
Pollution	Your CGL policy will exclude from coverage injury or damage arising out of the discharge of pollutants. Federal and state law strictly regulates the discharge of pollutants. Violation of those laws can result in fines and penalties totaling millions of dollars. Since virtually no insurance company is willing to insure these risks, strict attention to environmental compliance is absolutely necessary. One slight mistake with an environmental pollutant could bankrupt your business and/or land you in jail.
Workers' Compensation	Your CGL policy will not cover your obligations under workers' compensation laws. The law requires you to have workers' compensation insurance.
Care, Custody or Control	The policy generally will not cover damage to your property; property owned or rented by you; or property that is in your care, custody, or control.
Failure to Perform	Most policies will not cover the loss of use of property caused by your failure to perform the job correctly or because your products are not performing correctly.
Professional Liability	Separate policies are needed to insure against professional liability and/or errors and omissions.

Directors and Officers Liability	Otherwise known as D & O coverage, the Directors and Officers Liability policy provides protection to a company's directors and officers against claims for wrongful acts arising out of their duties to the corporation. For instance, if a member of the board of directors votes to enter into a contract that bankrupts the company, this coverage will protect him or her from claims that arose from his or her duties as a director, unless the court determines that the director was not reasonable in his or her decision. Stated another way, the director is covered by this policy unless he or she acts in reckless disregard of the consequences of his or her actions.
	This insurance will not cover intentional or illegal acts. For example, if a company officer voted to hire someone to assault a competing company's chairman, this coverage would not protect that officer. The assault would be an intentional, unlawful act not arising from his or her position as a director.
Installation Floaters	Installation floaters provide insurance against the value of goods and services installed at your risk at the project site. Installation floaters are advisable whenever expensive equipment is involved.
Builder's Risk	Builder's risk insurance is used to provide coverage on a project under construction. Depending on the contract, the coverage would be provided by either the owner or the contractor. That portion of the construction project that has been completed, together with the fixtures and equipment installed on the site, is insured by the builder's risk policy.
Key Man	If you are the owner of a relatively small business, this type of insurance coverage may be of great value to you. It insures the continuation of the business in the event of the death of a key employee. The corporation (limited liability company or partnership, as the case may be) purchases the insurance and is the named beneficiary. In the event of the key employee's death, the proceeds of the policy go to the corporation, or other entity, so that it can purchase the key employee's interest in the business.
CONCLUSION	Insurance is expensive. Therefore, carefully choose an agent, broker, or advisor that can give you the advice you need. Often, the insured will choose a policy with a larger than standard deductible in order to obtain a more affordable policy. In that case, the insured assumes the risk of claims that are less than the deductible. Additionally, most insurance companies will add coverage for warranty, completed operations, personal property, and other specialty risks, to your General Liability policy.

CHAPTER 3
ETHICS IN CONSTRUCTION

The application of the principles of project management is accomplished by people. Some people conduct their affairs without resorting to lying, cheating, or dealing unfairly with others. Others believe that the standard of conduct depends upon the facts of any given situation. These people believe that as situations change, they are allowed to change the manner in which they deal with others in order to achieve their final goals.

Most dictionaries define ethics in terms of a system of moral standards or a code of conduct governing an individual or a group. The word "standard" means something that remains constant, and "code" is a set of unchanging rules. Therefore, ethical behavior involves applying unvarying, fair principles to all situations.

For many, the decision to conduct one's business in an ethical manner is based upon religious or moral beliefs. However, the decision to deal honestly and fairly with others may also be based upon the desire to achieve success over the long term.

For purposes of this discussion, it is assumed that achieving the greatest success over the long run, both financial and otherwise, is preferred over larger short-term gains and fewer, if any, long-term gains. From a purely business standpoint, most would agree that a business plan that is calculated to yield steady growth and an enhanced reputation is preferred to a plan that seeks to capture larger short-term financial success while risking future earnings and reputation.

In the construction industry, the contractor will constantly be faced with decisions of an ethical and moral nature. Some people decide that they are willing to risk the consequences of stealing, cheating, and other criminal activities for the sake of greater short-term gains. The line between what is legal and what is illegal is fairly well defined. The line between what is ethical and what is unethical is not so clearly drawn. Many business people make their decisions based on whether or not an action has the potential of cutting into their long-term profit, if that action becomes public knowledge.

There is no way to consider all the kinds of ethical decisions that a contractor may face; however, let us consider four typical problems—bid rigging, bid shopping and chiseling, concealing defective work, and helping the architect or engineer cover up for defective design.

BID RIGGING

Bid rigging is conspiring with others to fix the outcome of a bid. This is usually done by colluding with some or all other bidders. The object of this exercise is to increase the profit on a project. Bid rigging is a crime, and, if caught, the contractor could be convicted of a felony. The risk is that others are necessarily involved, and, consequently, your future is in their hands. If these people are caught doing something improper, they may turn on you in order to save themselves.

BID SHOPPING

Bid shopping is disclosing one subcontractor's bid to another subcontractor in an effort to get a lower price. Bid shopping's first cousin, bid chiseling, is negotiating or beating a subcontractor down on the price. Neither of these two activities is a crime and neither is done in secret. However, such activities often result in a subcontractor submitting higher prices to general contractors who engage in such practices. The general contractor who lets the subcontractors know he will award the subcontract to the person whose price was low on bid day and at the price submitted is likely to get lower prices from the same subcontractors who submit higher prices to the other general contractors who shop or chisel their bids. It goes without saying that lower subcontractor prices result in more work and greater profit. Many general contractors do not consider bid shopping and beating a subcontractor down as unethical. However, regardless of what one calls them, these activities are likely to affect long-term profits.

CONCEALING DEFECTIVE WORK

Unfortunately, covering defective work is commonplace in the construction industry. The contractor who has a reputation for doing shoddy work is not likely to be chosen for a lot of work for private owners, once it is known that this is the case. Many believe that reputation means nothing on publicly bid projects; but owners and their architects and engineers are more likely to over inspect the work of a reputed shoddy builder. Furthermore, if defective work is uncovered, repair is always more costly than doing the work correctly the first time.

**COVERING
DESIGN FLAWS**

Sometimes an architect or engineer will make mistakes in the plans or specifications. These mistakes will usually be an error in the documents or an omission. It is not unheard of for the architect or engineer to ask the contractor to help him hide his mistake from the owner when a mistake results in extra costs. This is typically done by the architect's or engineer's approving a higher price on an unrelated change order. The temptation here is great because the contractor may have to work with the designer on future projects. From a business standpoint, the risk is that the owner may discover the conspiracy which is likely to result in a diminished reputation or worse. After one strips away all the justifications and rationalizations, this kind of activity is, at its core, dishonest, and engaging in dishonest behavior is a risk.

One cannot rely on what is lawful in order to determine what is correct behavior. Consider slavery and abortion for example. Many well-meaning people have historically taken opposite sides on these issues, which were, at different times, lawful and unlawful. Likewise, it is difficult to rely solely on religious principles to make ethical decisions.

It is not suggested here that laws and religious principles be abandoned. To the contrary, they should be considered in every decision. However, it may be more beneficial for a business person in the construction industry to consider the following two questions, when making hard ethical decisions:

◊ Is this an activity which I would not want everyone to know about?

◊ Is this the kind of behavior which is likely to support my long-term goals of sustained financial success and enhanced reputation?

CHAPTER 4
ESTIMATING

Estimating is the heart of the contracting business. The extremely competitive environment of the construction industry forces ever-smaller markups. Because of this, it is very important to have accurate estimates. In the manufacturing, wholesale, and retail sectors, the price of a product is determined after the costs have been established. In the construction industry, the price of the product is established before the actual cost has been determined. In the construction field, when costs are greater than expected, the company will lose money. No single management function is more important to the survival of a construction firm than accurate estimating. Accounting, cost control, scheduling, purchasing, and the actual construction work are all directly dependent on the estimate.

DEFINITION

Estimating is simply the process by which the contractor determines the cost of completing a project. This process entails compiling and analyzing all the items that contribute to the cost of the job, including materials, labor, equipment, and overhead costs.

There are two basic laws in construction estimating: first, low estimates decrease profits; and second, high estimates decrease volume. The goal should be an accurate cost estimate with an appropriate markup for overhead and profit.

BIDDING

Before doing all of the work required in preparing an estimate for a project, you must decide whether or not you want the job. Any project can be obtained: all that you have to do is submit a bid lower than anyone else's. Remember that there is a binding commitment to complete the project, if you are successful in obtaining the work.

Because you can spend a lot of time preparing cost estimates, you should prepare bids for only those projects you intend to complete and where you can be competitive with other bidders. If the prospect of making money on the job is questionable, bidding on it may not be appropriate.

In deciding whether or not to prepare a cost estimate and submit a bid, you must thoroughly evaluate the project. The main aspects to consider when evaluating a project are the type of work, the location of the work, unique on-site requirements, and the ability of the contractor to complete the project.

The key questions involved in the evaluation of the type of work on which to bid include the following:

◊ Does this project consist of the type of work the company does?

◊ Is the size of the project within the normal range of the company?

◊ Is the length of the job in line with the type of projects the company usually accepts?

Considerations should be paid to the location of the project. The distance to the project and the quality of the roads will affect not only the cost of conveying materials and equipment, but also the time lost through travel time of employees.

After deciding that the project looks good for the business, the process can move forward to the estimating phase.

THE ESTIMATING PROCESS

The system the contractor uses to develop estimates should be consistent and orderly. This system should follow the same sequence as the actual construction process. This helps to ensure that the estimator does not forget anything and helps schedule needed resources as the job progresses.

To produce accurate estimates, the process used by the contractor should rely on three things: a timely job cost system; a method to identify all of the material and equipment needed; and a method to predict the labor requirements of the project. For a complete discussion on maintaining a job cost system, see the accounting section (Chapter 8). Due to inflation, shortages, and other factors, the costs developed by the job cost system must be continually revised and verified against current prices. Frequently, the best output of a job cost system is the tracking of labor usage for particular tasks.

Accuracy In Estimating

Errors in developing cost estimates can have disastrous results for a construction company. If errors cause the estimate to be overstated (high), it will not be competitive and will likely result in the loss of the job. Errors that understate the cost of the job can leave you with a reduced profit or even a loss.

Estimating errors can result from many factors including:

◊ math errors, such as addition, subtraction, division, and decimal point placement errors;

◊ omission errors, such as failing to include cost or overhead items in the bid; and

◊ units of measure errors, such as using the wrong unit of measure or unit cost.

To keep errors to a minimum when preparing cost estimates, follow these steps:

◊ double check the math or have someone else check it;

◊ when multiplying and dividing, use the decimal equivalent of fractions to reduce errors;

◊ to avoid overlooking items, carefully read all the notes and specifications listed on the plans;

◊ carefully review the plans for missing sheets, duplicate sheets, scale used, etc.;

◊ use proper abbreviations for units of measure and materials;

◊ use checklists to help eliminate omissions and account for the different aspects of the job;

◊ verify that all items are being carried forward to the estimated detail sheets; and

◊ to aid in accurately accumulating costs, consistently use standard forms and formats for the take-off and cost estimate.

Estimating Methods

There are several estimating methods in use today. These range from a conceptual or architect's estimate to the detailed quantity survey method. The following list of methods is in order of *increasing* reliability.

Conceptual Estimate

The conceptual or architect's estimate approximates the actual construction cost. It is usually based on cost guides for similar projects. This estimate may vary a great deal from the contractor's actual cost.

Square Foot Method

The square foot method is a formula based on the floor area or square footage of a project. The job cost records for similar work provide the source for this method. This method is easy and quick to use and will give a rough approximation of the cost, but it does not consider inflation rates, style and quality differences, or other unique aspects of the project.

Cubic Foot Method	The cubic foot method is a variation of the square foot method and considers both the height of the wall and the floor area. This method is somewhat more accurate than the square foot method, but has the same disadvantages.
Components or Unit Price Method	The components or unit price method is a grouping of the component costs of an item into a particular unit in similar construction projects. For example, the cost of materials and labor for a 2x6 wood frame exterior wall, the cost of placing a 4-inch concrete slab, or the cost of exterior painting is expressed in square foot units for estimating purposes. This method provides a convenient way to compare other construction methods, and costs can be calculated with a minimum of detailed information.
Take-off or Quantity Survey Method	The take-off, or quantity survey, method is an accurate method that lists all the materials and labor needed for a construction project. This method lists the materials and equipment needed for a job and compiles the time required to install the materials and operate the equipment. Not only does this method provide a complete material list, but it also provides a simplified scheduling of the workflow; easier determination of purchasing and cash flow requirements; and better project organization.

MATERIAL TAKE-OFF

The quantity survey method requires a complete take-off of all materials that will be required for the project. This can be the most important part of the estimating process, as it is frequently the greatest cost component of a project.

Errors in compiling the materials needed for a particular project may result in overestimating the material costs. This results in turn with a higher bid that may cause you to be non-competitive with the other bidders and, consequently, to lose the job. Overestimating may result from:

◊   double counting items,

◊   including materials not needed,

◊   overpricing the cost of materials, or

◊   substituting higher priced items.

Underestimating the cost of materials will produce estimated costs that are lower than actual costs, resulting in lower than anticipated profits. If the errors are large enough, you can lose money on the project. Underestimating may result from:

◊ missing items during the take-off,

◊ under-pricing the cost of materials,

◊ under-estimating the cost of deliveries,

◊ including lower quality products than called for in the specifications, or

◊ estimating the amount of waste to be lower than it actually is.

To help keep errors to a minimum during the quantity take-off process, use checklists and material take-off forms. This will help reduce omissions, duplication, and the substitution of incorrect items. The material take-off forms will also help you schedule delivery of the materials to the jobsite. The material take-off forms can:

◊ group the types of materials to the various phases of the construction project;

◊ identify those items requiring long ordering lead times; and

◊ show items that may have special delivery problems.

By grouping the materials into logical construction phases, you can:

◊ reduce downtime by having the materials at the jobsite when needed;

◊ keep working capital needs to a minimum by scheduling deliveries of materials when they will be needed and not before; and

◊ reduce the exposure to loss by theft by having minimum inventory levels at the jobsite.

Lump sum quotes from material suppliers are preferable over unit cost quotes because, with a lump sum quote, the supplier submits a single bid for all materials necessary to complete a specific item of work. In unit cost material bids, a quantity take-off is required for each item of work and the supplier bids on the material list submitted by the contractor.

When developing the material estimate for a project, you must consider the waste or loss of materials at the jobsite. The best source for this aspect of the estimating process is the company's own historical data on similar construction projects.

Waste and loss of construction materials occur from:

◊   accidental breakage or spoilage,

◊   theft,

◊   weather, and

◊   normal waste due to the standard sizing of lumber, pipe, sheet goods, and other materials.

**ESTIMATING
LABOR COSTS**

Estimating the labor costs involved in a construction project is frequently the most difficult aspect of the estimating process. Because labor costs can make up anywhere from 25% to 100% of the hard costs of a project, accuracy is crucial in developing the estimate.

The first step in estimating the total cost of labor on a project is to determine the specific work to be done from the plans and specifications. This work should be organized by type of activity to make it easier to estimate the various time frames for the work.

Next, obtain the number of hours to do the listed tasks. This can be obtained either from the company's past performance records for similar work (job cost system) or from published labor tables showing labor units for the specific tasks. The use of labor tables has the advantage of providing consistency in labor estimating, but the tables should be modified based on job cost data and experience.

As with materials, several factors can affect the total cost and efficiency of the labor estimate. These factors include:

◊   weather conditions,

◊   skill of the crew,

◊   experience of the field management,

◊   type and availability of equipment,

◊   size of the crew for the particular job, and

◊   the time allotted for the project.

When estimating labor costs, be sure to include the non-productive time that will accumulate during construction. Such time may make up a sizeable portion of the lead man's time and time spent on:

◊ picking up materials,

◊ planning the work, and

◊ cleaning up.

After calculating the total hours for the various activities and making the necessary adjustments, multiply the result by the assigned standard and overtime wage rates as appropriate. Then add the labor overhead (or labor burden) to complete the labor portion of the estimate.

ESTIMATING EQUIPMENT NEEDS

The equipment costs vary tremendously by the type of project involved and the type of work conducted by the contractor. Some firms have limited equipment needs (such as a generator or compressor), while others have extensive requirements (such as large earthmoving equipment).

The first step in the estimating process for equipment is to identify the work that will require the use of specialized equipment. Next, the work involved must be matched to the particular type of equipment best suited to the work. After determining the type of equipment needed, calculate the number of hours or days required for the project.

The equipment needs of a given project may be satisfied by the following methods:

◊ using the contractor's own equipment,

◊ renting the needed equipment, or

◊ subcontracting the equipment portion to another contractor.

The calculations used to find the cost of the equipment needed on a project vary depending on the method used to fill the equipment needs. For example:

Owned Equipment

The cost of owned equipment is the cost to operate the item. It includes:

◊ a replacement cost factor based on the expected useful life of the item;

◊   operating costs, including fuel, oil, and lubricants;

◊   insurance;

◊   taxes and licenses; and

◊   operators.

Rented Equipment

Rented equipment cost is generally easier to calculate than for owned equipment, but it may be higher. Rented equipment costs consist of:

◊   the hourly, daily, weekly, or other rate for the equipment;

◊   any operating cost not included in the rental agreement; and

◊   the cost of operators.

Other Equipment Costs

Subcontractor equipment costs come from the bids received from subcontractors for the particular work involved.

Generally, project overhead includes the cost of tools required in the construction of the project and comes from the historical data for similar projects. If unusual requirements exist for tools on a particular job, they should be included in the equipment estimate.

ESTIMATING FOR SECURITY NEEDS

Loss of construction materials through theft can be minimized by taking the following steps:

◊   keeping inventory levels as low as practical by scheduling materials for delivery as close to their use as possible;

◊   using locked storage trailers for small items;

◊   bundling wood products and like items into large, heavy clusters;

◊   fencing the jobsite; and

◊   hiring security guards.

ESTIMATING OVERHEAD

Besides the hard cost components of an estimate, an allowance must be made for the overhead costs associated with contracting. Overhead costs consist of project overhead costs and company or administrative overhead expenses.

Project Overhead

Project overhead costs are costs that relate to the construction activity itself but are not easily identifiable costs of a given project. They may consist of costs associated with several projects. For example, project costs generally include the following items:

◊ supervisor salaries,

◊ permits and fees,

◊ construction supplies,

◊ small tools,

◊ cleanup costs,

◊ barricades,

◊ bonds,

◊ sanitary facilities,

◊ storage trailers, and

◊ temporary utilities.

Company Overhead

As opposed to project overhead costs, which occur only when construction work is underway, company overhead expenses continue even when no work is underway. Company overhead expenses consist of the costs of running a business. Typical company overhead expenses include the following:

◊ office salaries,

◊ office rent,

◊ company insurance,

◊ accounting and legal fees,

◊ telephone,

◊ office utilities,

◊ postage,

◊ taxes,

◊ advertising costs, and

◊ office supplies.

You should base the calculations of the project and company overhead rates on historical data.

CALCULATING OVERHEAD

In order to submit accurate bids, overhead must be added to the other components of the bid. Overhead rates are estimated or forecasted at the beginning of the year, based on past performance and any anticipated changes in the coming year.

For example, assume that the following changes to the amounts shown on the sample income statement (see Chapter 8) are expected for the new year.

	Current Year	Current Percent	Anticipated Increase
Revenues	$1,077,760		$250,000
Project O/H	95,410	8.9%	20,000
G & A Expenses	161,260	14.9%	12,500

The new overhead percentages used for bidding would be calculated as follows:

Project Overhead:	$\dfrac{95,410 \;+\; 20,000}{1,077,760 \;+\; 250,000}$	$=\;8.7\%$
Company Overhead:	$\dfrac{161,260 \;+\; 12,500}{1,077,760 \;+\; 250,000}$	$=\;13.1\%$

To illustrate the use of these overhead percentages in the bidding process, assume that a proposed job has $250,000 in direct costs, and a 10% before tax profit is desired. The following calculations will obtain the correct amount to bid:

Project O/H	8.7%
Company O/H	13.1%
Profit (before taxes)	10.0%
Combined O/H & Profit	31.8%
Total Bid	100.0%
Less O/H & Profit	(31.8%)
Equals Direct Costs	68.2%

Therefore, the bid price is:

$$\frac{\$250,000}{.682} \;=\; \$366,569$$

To recap the bid:

Bid amount	$366,569	100%
Direct costs	(250,000)	(68.2%)
Project O/H	(31,892)	(8.7%)
Gross Profit	84,677	23.1%
Company O/H	(48,020)	(13.1%)
Before tax profit	$36,657	10.0%

ADDING PROFIT

The essential element in the construction business is to be profitable and competitive. If the markup is too low, there may be an insufficient cushion to protect the contractor if actual costs exceed those estimated. Often the low bidder is the one with the least markup for profit, the lowest overhead, or a combination of the two.

The average profit margin in the construction industry over the past few years has been about 5%. Profit should be sufficient to provide the owners with a return on their investment and provide for the continued growth of the business.

Typically, the same markup for profit applies to all jobs, unless a reason exists to do otherwise. If the desirability of a project is low or certain abnormal risks exist, the markup for profit may be increased. If, on the other hand, the company needs work badly to keep valuable employees and cover company overhead, a lower than normal markup may be added.

CONTROL

As someone once said, "If we don't learn from our mistakes, we are destined to repeat them." To prevent estimation errors, a control function must be in place to compare the actual costs incurred on a project to its estimated costs. The objective of this process is to detect the problems or mistakes made when estimating a project and to correct those errors or inefficiencies.

CHAPTER 5
SCHEDULING

In the estimating section, we saw that the quantity survey process determines what is needed for a construction project. The scheduling phase controls when those resources will be needed. By determining what is needed when, it becomes possible to establish what resources are required for any project at any time.

Because most of us cannot visually track all the complex activities of a construction project in our heads, it is necessary to rely on written aids. These aids are designed to make the construction process more efficient and reduce the time it takes to complete a project. When the construction time can be shortened, costs will also be reduced. Most project overhead costs and interest expense relate directly to time. Therefore, reducing the length of time to complete a project will also reduce these costs.

A good scheduling system can provide several benefits, including:

◊   Workflow can be distributed evenly, reducing slack time.

◊   Material orders can be controlled to consider long lead times for items that are difficult to obtain. To minimize stockpiling, delivery of materials can also be scheduled to coincide with their use.

An organized workplace increases worker morale, thereby increasing productivity and commitment.

The disadvantages of a formalized scheduling system include the cost of installing the system, training personnel, and gaining the acceptance of those who will use the system.

Implementing a project scheduling system involves three distinct phases:

◊   Planning

◊   Scheduling

◊   Controlling

PLANNING

The goal of the planning process is to find the best combination of resources needed for the various activities. Ideally, the same activities that were defined in the estimating quantity take-off phase can be used to plan the resources needed in the scheduling phase. This prevents duplicating effort.

The planning process involves listing all the *materials*, *manpower*, *money*, and *machinery* (4 m's) necessary to complete a project in activity or segment phases. The process then determines the time required to complete each activity and the relationships of the various activities to each other.

The next step is to compile all the activities (or tasks) into a complete project plan and prepare a schedule.

SCHEDULING

The project schedule is nothing more than a plan with time applied. The activity phases defined in the planning process come together in the schedule according to when they can and should be completed. By summing the project activities into an overall schedule, you can determine the total resource demand for a project at any time.

The type of scheduling system that a contractor should use depends on several factors, including the following:

◊   the type of construction work the firm specializes in;

◊   whether the work will be done by the contractor's own employees or by subcontractors;

◊   the volume of work currently underway and anticipated;

◊   the size, location, and complexity of the projects;

◊   the ability of the contractor's staff; and

◊   the extent of requirements imposed by lenders, owner, contract provisions, and other factors.

Scheduling systems vary from a simple "to do" list to a sophisticated interdependent time scale system. The common types of scheduling systems in use today include lists, time scale or bar charts, and interdependent time scales. Due to its limited use in residential projects, the interdependent time scale system is not covered here.

The list method is merely a "to do" list of activities. It also may include completion dates, contract responsibilities, requirements, and other items. This type of scheduling system is generally appropriate for small operations, simple projects, or single-activity contractors.

Time scale (Gantt charts) or bar charts reflect when an activity should take place and its expected duration. This is a very common method of scheduling in the construction industry. The primary weakness of this method is that it does not show the dependency of activities to each other. The illustration on the following page shows a basic bar chart for a residential construction project.

BAR CHART FOR HOUSE

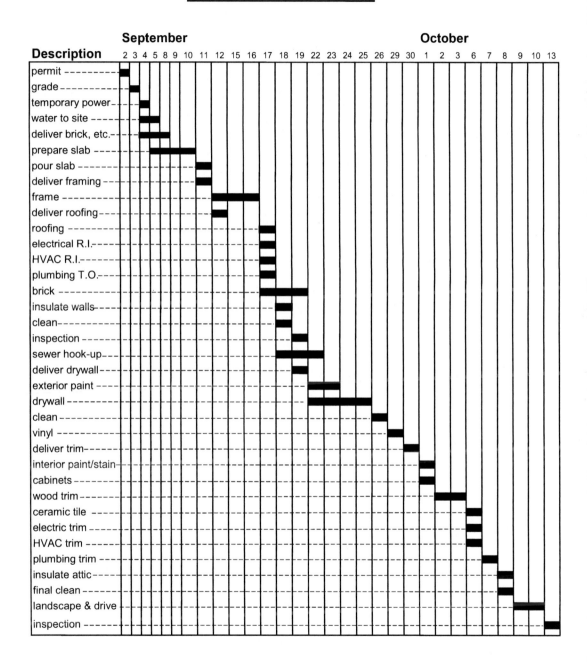

Reprinted with permission from *Scheduling for Builders* by Jerry Householder, National Association of Home Builders, 1201 15th St., NW, Washington, DC 20005

As a general rule, the best project schedule is the simplest one that can economically complete the project on time.

CASH FLOW SCHEDULE

Another important aspect of scheduling is plotting the cash flow requirements of a given project. The cash flow schedule identifies the expected dollar amounts of progress payments and disbursements and when these receipts and outlays occur. The timing of receipts is based on the scheduled completion of activities and the payment terms in the contract. The estimating process identifies the disbursements.

The cash flow schedule is important because it reflects the working capital need at any given time during the project. If the contractor does not have sufficient working capital, the schedule identifies the extent of financing that must be obtained over the course of the project. Additionally, financing costs can be determined and factored into the bid. The following cumulative cash flow graph illustrates the progress payments received (line A) and disbursements (line B) for the project. The difference between the cumulative inflows and outflows at any point reflect the cash shortfall (or excess) from the project. Any shortfall must be made up from the contractors own funds or from outside financing. Knowing the working capital needs of a project ahead of time can avert a cash crunch and possible contract default during construction.

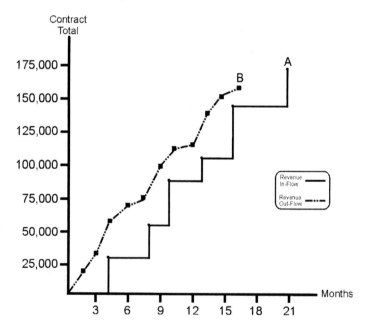

**CONTROL
FUNCTION**

The prospect that all will automatically go well after the completion of the planning and scheduling is unlikely. All the estimating, planning, and scheduling work make for the potential of a profitable project, but the control function is the one that can make the potential a reality.

Project control involves monitoring the job costs and comparing these actual costs to the progress reached on the project and the anticipated costs to that point. It is essential to monitor costs to document production inefficiencies and deviations and to implement corrective action.

Frequently a contractor will not find out if a project makes a profit or a loss until he or she pays all of the bills and receives the final draw. Using a job cost system (see Chapter 8) to collect the labor, material, equipment, and project overhead cost data will not only measure the performance on the current project but aid future bidding activities.

CHAPTER 6
ENVIRONMENTAL & SAFETY
CONSIDERATIONS

For pollution control purposes, the environment must be perceived as interrelated and often interchangeable. A single source may pollute the air with smoke and chemicals; the land with solid wastes; and a river or lake with chemical and other wastes. Some pollutants, like chemicals, radiation, and pesticides, can appear in many different forms. Air pollution can take on many different forms; it can produce solid wastes, which then pollute the land or water. Water-polluting effluent may convert it into solid wastes, which must be disposed of on land.

THE EPA

The mission of the U.S. Environmental Protection Agency (EPA) is to protect human health and to safeguard the natural environment—air, water, and land—upon which life depends. More than a dozen major statutes or laws form the legal basis for the programs of the Environmental Protection Agency (EPA). Among these is the Occupational Safety and Health Act (OSHA).

DESIGN AND SITE CONSIDERATIONS

Design considerations are one of the most important parts of any project undertaking. Without a proper design that incorporates environmental protection and safety requirements tailored for the site location, problems will likely be encountered. These problems could result in the loss of time and money for the employer.

When designing a project, many variables need to be taken into account, including:

◊ the area where work is being done (such as urban, rural, desert, or forest);

◊ the type of work being performed;

◊ the different types of materials needed on the jobsite, and how many of them are on the EPA hazardous materials list (there are currently over 500 materials on the list);

◊ safety precautions required for hazardous materials present on the jobsite;

◊ drainage patterns at the start of the project and how they will change at different times throughout the project; and

◊   where on-site equipment maintenance will be performed (keeping contamination of oils, solvents, and chemicals in one location).

WATER QUALITY

The Clean Water Act prohibits the discharge of any pollutants into any navigable waters of the United States, unless the discharge is allowed by a National Pollutant Discharge Elimination System (NPDES) permit. Efforts to reduce water pollution originally focused on sewage treatment plants and industrial sites. Later, it became evident that there were other sources of water pollution, such as construction site runoff from storm water and other water used on the site. Along with sediment, construction activities have pollutants, such as pesticides, construction chemicals, petroleum products, solvents, asphalts, and acids that can contaminate water runoff.

It was found that construction site runoff was typically 10 to 20 times greater than that from agricultural lands, and 1,000 to 2,000 times greater than forest lands. It is quite easy to see that, in a short period of time, construction activity can discharge more sediment and pollutants into the water system than natural sources will over decades.

In 1987, changes were made to the Clean Water Act that required the EPA to implement regulations for the NPDES Storm Water Program. The first phase of these regulations was developed in 1990 and covered the discharge of storm water associated with construction activity disturbing five or more acres. This is referred to as Phase I, or large construction activity source.

The second phase of these regulations (Storm Water Phase II Rules) became final in 1999 and covers:

◊   regulated small Municipal Separate Storm Sewer Systems (MS4s), and

◊   "small" construction activity that involves from one to five acres.

Site activities disturbing less than one acre are also regulated as small construction activity under certain conditions. For example, if they are part of a larger common plan of development that involves an area greater than one acre and less than five acres, they are regulated. They can also be regulated if it is determined by the NPDES permitting authority that there is a potential for contribution to a violation of a water quality standard, or for a significant contribution of pollutants to waters of the United States.

Under the Phase II Rules, NPDES permitting authorities have the authority to provide a waiver from the requirements to the operators of a small construction activity.

Permits are not yet needed. Specific compliance dates for Phase II implementation will be set by each NPDES permitting authority as changes to the appropriate regulations are made.

A construction site operator is defined by EPA as a person who has operational control of the project's plans and specifications, including the ability to make modifications to those plans and specifications. An operator can also include a person who has day-to-day operational control of those activities that are necessary to ensure compliance with a storm water pollution prevention plan (SWPPP) for the site.

AIR QUALITY

The predominant part of the nation's population is located in its rapidly expanding metropolitan and other urban areas. These areas generally cross the boundary lines of local jurisdictions and often extend into two or more states. The growth in the amount and complexity of air pollution brought about by urbanization, industrial development, and the increasing use of motor vehicles has resulted in mounting dangers to the public health and welfare, including injury to agricultural crops and livestock, damage and deterioration of property, and hazards to air and ground transportation. Air pollution prevention (that is, the reduction or elimination of the amount of pollutants produced or created at the source) and air pollution control at its source are the primary responsibility of states and local governments.

Dust in the air from construction sites adds greatly to the particulate matter in the air and adds to air pollution. This problem has come under scrutiny from the EPA; it is a serious problem that can be easily remedied with water. To avoid costly fines, contractors need to pay close attention to any dust they are creating.

UNDERGROUND STORAGE

Underground storage should be considered a system, and not just a large container that holds a product. The storage tank is a system consisting of the holding tank, the piping to carry to product for filling and discharging product, piping that connects multiple tanks, pumps, and a method or methods to detect any release of product from any part of the system.

The term "Underground Storage Tank" (UST) includes any combination of tanks and underground pipes connected to the tanks that are used to contain a regulated substance. To qualify as a UST, the volume of the tank and underground pipes must be ten percent or more beneath the surface of the ground. The following items are not included in the definition of a UST:

◊   surface impounds, pits, ponds, or lagoons;

◊   storm water or waste water collection system; and

◊   any storage tank situated in an underground area (such as a basement or cellar) if the storage tank is situated upon or above the surface of the floor.

SOLID AND HAZARDOUS WASTE

According to the EPA regulations, solid waste means any garbage (refuse), sludge from a wastewater treatment plant, water supply treatment plant, or air pollution control facility. It also includes other discarded material, including solid, liquid, semi-solid, or contained gaseous material resulting from construction, industrial, commercial, mining, and agricultural operations, and from community activities.

The Resource Conservation and Recovery Act (RCRA) was enacted in 1976 to protect human health and the environment from the potential hazards of waste disposal; to conserve energy and natural resources; to reduce the amount of waste generated; and to ensure that wastes are managed in an environmentally sound manner. The RCRA regulates the management of solid waste (e.g., garbage), hazardous waste, and underground storage tanks holding petroleum products or certain chemicals.

Wastes that exhibit certain characteristics may be regulated by the RCRA. A waste may be considered hazardous if it is ignitable (i.e., burns readily), corrosive, or reactive (e.g., explosive). Waste may also be considered hazardous if it contains certain amounts of toxic chemicals. In addition to these characteristic wastes, EPA has also developed a list of over 500 specific hazardous wastes. Hazardous waste may take different physical forms and may be solid, semi-solid, or even liquid.

A few of the materials that may be generated at a construction site and are considered industrial and hazardous waste include:

◊   batteries,

◊   used oil,

◊   spilled or used fuel, and

◊   cleaning solvents and chemicals.

The category of "mixed waste" contains a combination of radioactive and hazardous waste (such as industrial, or medical). A dual regulatory framework exists for mixed waste, with the EPA or states regulating the hazardous waste, and the Nuclear Regulatory Commission (NRC) or the Department of Energy (DOE) regulating the radioactive waste. The NRC generally regulates commercial and non-DOE federal facilities. The DOE is currently self-regulating; its orders apply to DOE sites and contractors.

ENVIRONMENTAL ECONOMICS

Failure to follow environmental regulations and thereby contribute to pollution can have serious economic repercussions, including:

◊   being assessed for the harm caused to the environment;

◊   paying the cleanup costs associated with the damage done;

◊   receiving fines and citations; and

◊   the potential loss of licenses.

IMPORTANCE OF SAFETY

The importance of safety at the construction site cannot be overstated. It is the responsibility of both the contractor and the employees to maintain a safe and healthy working environment.

Because construction sites can be dangerous, employees must continually be alert and use common sense as they do their jobs. The contractor and employees should watch constantly for possible hazards at the jobsite and take whatever action is necessary to correct hazards. This is true even if safety regulations do not require the changes.

Safety is not something that just happens; as with other aspects of the construction process, it must be planned, placed into operation, checked for effectiveness, and modified as needed. Some people in the construction industry have resisted the implementation of safety and health standards, but the fact remains that, by law, safety and health standards are required and may get stricter.

Employees in the construction industry have the right to work in a safe and healthy environment. Employers have the responsibility to take the necessary precautions to provide safe and sanitary working conditions. In some situations, not all of the danger at a jobsite can be eliminated. In these cases, the dangers should be identified and proper safety procedures put in place.

Having an attitude of "let's wait and see if we have an accident" and then just reacting to any accidents that occur, also known as "knee-jerk safety management", can be disastrous in the construction business. Contractors need to have a defined safety program in place, from the start of a construction project.

Several factors should motivate contractors to prepare a working safety program. These factors include the following:

◊ employer losses,

◊ employee losses,

◊ safety and health regulations, and

◊ legal consequences.

A major part of project cost control is preventing accidents. To get the most out of a safety program, the program must try to reduce the causes of construction injuries or illnesses.

EMPLOYER LOSSES

Safety-related losses could affect you in many ways, including the following examples:

◊ time lost on the job could cause a missed deadline;

◊ higher insurance rates due to a poor safety record (this can be important when bidding for a job against a contractor with a good safety record);

◊ the repair or replacement costs of damaged equipment or materials;

◊ the loss of the services of highly trained workers;

◊ lower productivity from workers when they view their working environment as unsafe;

◊ the loss of a good image of the company, which makes it harder to obtain future work; and

◊ citations and fines assessed for not following safety regulations.

EMPLOYEE LOSSES

Losses to employees that can result because of accidents occurring on the job include:

◊ loss of wages,

◊ pain and suffering caused by an accident,

◊ possible loss of the ability to work at the same job,

◊ possible harm to the worker's family,

◊ possible loss of life,

◊ mental or emotional problems that can arise out of an injury, and

◊ personal loss of self-esteem.

Although some of the items listed above are intangible and difficult to put a price on, lawsuit settlements often include very high amounts for the intangible injuries that workers sustain.

CONSEQUENCES OF IGNORING SAFETY REGULATIONS

Failure to conform to federal or state safety regulations can create a number of legal problems for the contractor. Problems from the following occurrences may be so severe as to result in the loss of the business:

◊ Fines can be assessed against the contractor for failure to take proper safety precautions, as prescribed by law.

◊ Fines can be assessed against the contractor for failure to provide proper training to his or her employees.

◊ The firm may be barred from bidding on future contracts.

◊ The contractor's license may be subjected to disciplinary action that could result in its revocation.

◊ Civil lawsuits may be filed against the contractor. With the current climate of extremely high court settlements in civil lawsuits, a single lawsuit could put a contractor out of business.

◊ An indefinite liability may be created by lingering health problems from injuries that cause long-term emotional, mental, or physical disabilities.

A poor or non-functioning safety program can provide the impression that the contractor was interested only in making money and had little regard for the safety of the employees. In contrast, a complete and properly implemented safety program that not only meets regulatory standards, but also surpasses them, can be used to show that the company was not negligent in its duty to the employees, and was even going to extra lengths to safeguard them.

Clearly, the cost of injuries is a major concern in keeping a business in healthy financial condition. A comprehensive safety program can save money and provide many intangible benefits. Because people are the most important part of the construction industry, it makes sense that keeping the workers healthy is just good business. A safe and healthy work place helps create a productive and cost efficient jobsite.

FEDERAL REGULATIONS

There are two federal safety regulations that have a direct impact on the construction industry. The first is the Construction Safety Act of 1969 (CSA) and the second is the Williams-Steiger Occupational Safety and Health Act of 1970 (OSHA).

Construction Safety Act

The Construction Safety Act applies to contracting work that uses federal funds. This act places restrictions on working conditions that are dangerous or unsanitary.

Occupational Safety and Health Act (OSHA)

The Occupational Safety and Health Act created safety and health regulations that cover almost all of the employees in the private sector. When the act was written, the safety provisions of the CSA were included.

States are encouraged to develop their own safety and health plans. These plans must be at least as effective as the federal law. Twenty-five states have adopted the OSHA, and twenty-three of these states require coverage in both the private and public sectors. Frequently, safety and health concerns that are unique to a state are added to the provisions.

CONTRACTOR OBLIGATIONS

Under the provisions of the safety regulations, contractors have specific obligations to their employees. These obligations include the following:

◊ knowing the safety and health programs available from the Department of Labor;

◊ instructing each employee on safe equipment operation, the recognition and avoidance of unsafe conditions, potential hazards, and the regulations that apply to the job;

◊ instructing each employee on the proper procedures to use to avoid injury, if any unusual or potentially unsafe condition is present, and on the proper emergency procedures to use if an accident or injury occurs; and

◊ providing first aid services for every employee covered by the act.

**Emergency
Action Plan**

The contractor is responsible for having an emergency action plan. He or she is responsible for training employees on how the plan works and on how it will be implemented. The plan should be in writing and located in a convenient area of the work place so that employees may review it. The only exception is for contractors with 10 or fewer employees. In this case, the plan does not have to be in writing and may be communicated orally to the employees.

From a liability standpoint, not maintaining a written plan is risky. If the contractor does not have a written plan because of an exemption under the law, then, as a protection, the contractor should have the employees sign a form acknowledging their briefing of the oral emergency action plan. If there is no evidence of a plan or employee training, the contractor is likely to be found at fault for any accident that occurs.

**Reporting & Record
Keeping
Requirements**

An injury or illness meets the general recording criteria, if it results in death, days away from work, restricted work, or transfer to another job, medical treatment beyond first aid, or loss of consciousness. A case also meets the general recording criteria if it involves a significant injury or illness diagnosed by a physician or other licensed health care professional. Significant aggravation of a pre-existing condition by a workplace event or exposure makes the case work-related and reportable.

Companies, with ten or fewer employees at all times during the last calendar year, do not need to maintain OSHA injury and illness records unless OSHA or the BLS (Bureau of Labor Statistics) informs them in writing that they must maintain the records. If a company had more than ten employees at any time during the prior calendar year, it is not exempt and must keep OSHA injury and illness records. However, all employers covered by the OSHA Act must report to OSHA any workplace incident that results in a fatality, including all fatal heart attacks or the hospitalization of three or more employees.

The 300 and 300A forms replace the Form 200, Log and Summary of Occupational Injuries and Illnesses. Form 301, Injury and Illness Incident Report, replaces Form 101, Supplementary Record of Occupational Injuries and Illnesses. Employers are not required to update their old 200 and 101 forms for years before 2002.

These forms and reports now required by OSHA include the following:

◊ Form 300, Log of Work–Related Injuries and Illness. Each documented occupational injury or illness must be logged on this form.

◊ Form 301, Injury and Illness Incident Report, provides data on how the injury or illness occurred.

◊ Form 300A, Summary of Work-Related Injuries and Illness, provides additional data to make it easier for employers to calculate incident rates. Employers must review 300 Log information before it is summarized on the 300A form. A company executive is required to certify the accuracy of the summary. This summary is to be posted for a three-month period.

Copies of Form 300, Form 300A, and Form 301 are reprinted at the end of this chapter.

Employers must retain the OSHA records for five years from the end of the year to which they relate. The employer must provide copies of the retained records to authorized government representatives, to their employees, and to employee representatives.

Exposure records and data analysis of them must be kept for 30 years. Medical records must be kept for the duration of employment, plus 30 years. Records do not have to be maintained for employees that have worked for the employer less than one year, but the employer must provide these records to the employee upon termination. If a contractor ceases to do business and there is no successor to receive the records, the employer must advise the current employees at least three months prior to ceasing business, and make the employees' records available to them. The National Institute for Occupational Safety and Health must be notified in writing at least three months prior to the disposal of any records.

All employers, regardless of the number of employees, must display the OSHA poster. Within eight hours of an accident, they must report the death of any employee (including all fatal heart attacks) or an incident that requires hospitalization of three or more employees. This also applies to any such fatality or hospitalization of three or more employees that occurs within 30 days of an accident.

Maximum flexibility has been provided so employers can keep all the information on computers, at a central location, or on alternate forms, as long as the information is compatible and the data can be produced when required. Employers must provide records to an OSHA compliance officer who requests them within four business hours.

Construction work sites that are scheduled to continue for a year or more must maintain a separate 300 Log. The log may be maintained either at the construction site, or a central location as long as the employer can transmit information about the injuries and illnesses to the central location within seven calendar days of receiving information that a recordable injury or illness has occurred.

EMPLOYEE INVOLVEMENT

Employers are required to establish a process for employees to report injuries and illnesses. Employers are prohibited from discriminating against employees who do report an injury or illness. Employees are allowed to access the 301 forms to review records of their own injuries and illnesses. Employee representatives are allowed to access those parts of the 301 form that relates to workplace safety and health.

PROTECTING PRIVACY

Employers are required to protect employee's privacy by withholding an individual's name on Form 300 for certain types of sensitive injuries or illnesses (e.g., sexual assaults, HIV infections, mental illnesses, etc). Employers are allowed to withhold descriptive information about sensitive injuries in cases where not doing so would disclose the employee's identity. Employee representatives are given access only to the portion of Form 301 that contains information about the injury or illness, while personal information about the employee and his or her health care provider is withheld. Employers are required to remove employees' names before providing injury and illness data to persons who do not have access rights.

**INJURY
DECISION TREE
OSHA 1904**

The decision, as to whether a particular injury or illness is recordable, involves several steps.

For recording work-related injuries and illnesses, the injury decision tree shows the steps involved in making this determination.

INJURY DECISION TREE

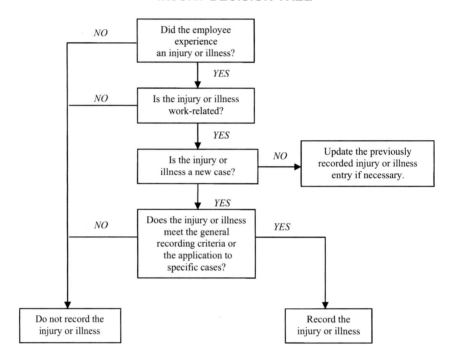

PENALTIES

On-site inspections by OSHA personnel can result in the reporting of safety violations, the issuance of citations, and the assessing of penalties. OSHA has been increasing the number of citations it issues, as well as the size of the fines. For example, in 1983 OSHA imposed penalties of $4.8 million. In 2002, federal and state inspectors found 222,000 violations during 95,000 inspections and assessed $148.7 million in penalties! Over 50% of the citations involved construction projects. It is not uncommon for an employer's first inspection by OSHA to result in multiple citations amounting to thousands of dollars.

If a citation is issued to the employer, a copy of that citation must be posted near the place of the violation for a period of three days or until the violation has been remedied. The employer has the right to appeal any penalties assessed. He or she can use various methods to appeal the citation, ranging from informal meetings to court hearings.

In an attempt to improve safety, OSHA can provide jobsite consultation services on safety and health issues. These services are available at no cost to the employer and are confidential. No citations or any other penalties are assessed against the employer during these courtesy visits.

VIOLATION TYPES

Citations for violations many be issued for a variety of reasons. These reasons range from total disregard of safety procedures to failure to properly post documents. The seven categories of violations are as follows:

◊ **Willful** – A violation is considered to be willful when an employer intentionally commits a violation with indifference to the law or allows a known hazardous condition to exist. In addition to the citations and penalties that OSHA can impose, the U.S. Department of Justice can file criminal charges against an employer whose willful violation of a standard resulted in the death of an employee.

◊ **Repeated** – A violation of any standard, rule, regulation, or order where, during a re-inspection, a substantially similar violation is found. The original citation must be final for the new violation to be considered a repeat violation.

◊ **Serious** – A violation that the employer knew, or should have known, had a high probability that serious physical harm or death could result.

◊ **Other than Serious** – A violation that is directly related to the health and safety of the employees, but is not likely to cause serious physical harm or death.

◊ **Failure to Abate** – After the prescribed correction date, this penalty can be assessed for each day the violation continues.

◊ **Falsifying Records, Reports, or Applications** – Deliberately making false records and reports.

◊ **Ignoring Posting Requirements** – Failure to post the required OSHA posters, citations, and documentation.

The following table shows a schedule of the penalties that OSHA can impose on a contractor for the various violations listed.

Types of Violations	Penalty
Willful Violation	$5,000 to $70,000
Willful with a Fatality First Conviction	$250,000 to $500,000 and/or 6 month imprisonment
Willful with a Fatality Second Conviction	$250,000 to $500,000 and/or 1 year imprisonment
Repeated Violation	$5,000 to $70,000
Serious Violation	$100 to $7,000
Other than Serious Violation	Up to $7,000
Failure to Abate Violation	Up to $7,000 per day
Falsifying Records, Reports, or Applications Violation	Up to $10,000 and/or 6 months imprisonment
Ignoring Posting Requirements	Up to $7,000

ADJUSTMENT OF PENALTIES

Penalties for non-willful violations may be adjusted down based on several factors, including company size, as shown on the table below.

Number of Employees	% Reduction
1-25	60
26-100	40
101-250	20
251 or more	None

Other adjustment factors that may be allowed in addition to company size include the following:

◊ the seriousness of the violation;

◊ the fact that the employer is making a good faith effort to provide good workplace health and safety;

◊ the employer has demonstrated good faith by having an approved written and implemented safety and health program; and

◊ the history of employer's OSHA citations for serious, willful, or repeated violations.

MATERIAL SAFETY DATA SHEET

Chemical manufacturers and importers are required to develop a material safety data sheet (MSDS) for each hazardous chemical they produce or import. The information must be in English and distributors are responsible for providing their customers with copies of these MSDSs. Employers are responsible for having an MSDS on hand for each hazardous chemical they use.

The role of the MSDSs is to provide detailed information on hazardous chemicals and their effects. OSHA regulations require that specific information be made available to employees using hazardous chemicals. During an OSHA site inspection, compliance officers will evaluate the following elements of a contractor's MSDS program:

◊ if MSDS information is current and how it is updated;

◊ if there is MSDS access in the employee work area;

◊ the designation of the person responsible for obtaining and maintaining the sheets;

◊ how the MSDSs are maintained in the workplace; and

◊ how the employees are given training and information prior to working with hazardous materials.

The American National Standards Institute (ANSI), working with the Chemical Manufacturers' Association (CMA) has developed a standard format for material safety data sheets. The typical information found in an MSDS includes:

◊ product name of the material, as used on the label;

◊ manufacturer's name, address, phone number, and emergency phone number;

◊ the date of preparation or last editing of the data;

◊ chemical name and common name;

◊ if the chemical is a mixture, the chemical and common names of all ingredients over 1% that present a health or physical hazard;

◊ physical and chemical characteristics of the hazardous chemical (flash point, vapor pressure, water solubility, appearance, and odor);

◊ fire and explosion data (flash point, flammable limits, extinguishing media, unusual fire and explosion hazards, special fire fighting procedures, stability, and incompatibility with other materials);

◊ health hazard data (routes of entry into the body, acute and chronic health hazards, signs and symptoms of exposure, carcinogenicity, medical conditions aggravated by exposure, emergency and first aid procedures, waste disposal, and handling precautions); and

◊ control measures (type of respiratory protection, protective clothing needed, ventilation, work/hygienic procedures, and proper storage and handling).

OCCUPATIONAL NOISE EXPOSURE

Protection against the effects of noise exposure must be provided to employees when the sound levels exceed those shown in the table on the following page, as measured on the A scale of a standard sound level meter at slow response.

When employees are subjected to sound levels exceeding those listed in the table, the employer must initiate administrative or engineering controls. If such controls fail to reduce sound levels to safe levels, the employer must provide personal protective equipment to reduce sound levels to the allowable levels.

In all cases where the sound levels exceed the values shown on the following page, the employee must administer a continuing, effective hearing conservation program.

PERMISSIBLE NOISE EXPOSURES

Sound level duration per day in hours	Decibels Scale A slow response
8	90
6	92
4	95
3	97
2	100
1 1/2	102
1	105
1/2	110
1/4 or less	115

When the daily noise exposure is composed of two or more periods of noise exposure of different levels, their combined, rather than individual, effect should be considered. Exposure to impulsive or impact noise should not exceed the 140 dB peak sound pressure level.

ASBESTOS

In the construction industry today, there are very few products being installed that contain any of the minerals in a group of materials called asbestos. Unfortunately, this was not always common practice. Contractors who deal with older buildings must know if any of these products are present and if their workers are at risk.

Because asbestos products have a high resistance to heat, electrical, and chemical conditions, as well as strength, it is easy to see how so many asbestos-containing products were used in the construction industry in years gone by. Asbestos was commonly found in such products as insulation, cement pipe, acoustical products, floor tile, and shingles, to name just a few.

The danger of asbestos products comes from asbestos' small fibers that enter the body by being either breathed in or swallowed. Fibers can be so small that someone working with the material may not be aware of what is happening. The fibers become imbedded in the lungs and stomach. This exposure can be very harmful and even fatal because it can cause severe respiratory problems, along with several forms of cancer. The symptoms may not appear for 20 years or more.

OSHA began regulating exposure to asbestos products in the workplace in 1970. In 1994, OSHA issued final standards regulating workplace exposure to asbestos (29 CFR. 1926.1101). The standards do the following:

◊ set permissible exposure limits (PEL) to asbestos;

◊ specify the medical surveillance and record keeping requirements;

◊ detail the training required of a competent person to safeguard the health and safety of the workers on the jobsite;

◊ require exposure assessments and monitoring; and

◊ require the posting of warning signs and the isolation of the regulated work area.

The standards apply when material containing more than 1% asbestos is involved in the following activities:

◊ demolition or salvage of structures;

◊ removal or encapsulation of materials;

◊ construction, alteration, repair, maintenance, or renovation of products containing asbestos;

◊ spills or emergency cleanup of asbestos materials; and

◊ transportation, disposal, storage, or containment at the jobsite.

LEAD

Lead is commonly added to industrial paints because of its ability to resist corrosion. Construction work involving welding, cutting, brazing, and blasting on lead paint surfaces can result in lead exposures. Ingesting and inhaling lead represents the typical forms of exposure in contaminated workplaces.

The rate of lead absorption into the body depends on its chemical and physical form and on the physiological characteristics of the exposed person. Once in the blood, lead is distributed to the soft tissue (kidney, bone marrow, liver, and brain) and the bones and teeth.

At many jobsites, a regular schedule of housekeeping activities to remove accumulations of lead dust and lead-containing debris is necessary to keep airborne lead levels at or below permissible exposure limits. Vacuuming is considered the most reliable method of cleaning dusty surfaces, but any effective method may be used (for example, a wet floor scrubber). When vacuuming equipment is used, the vacuums must be equipped with high-efficiency particulate air (HEPA) filters. Blowing with compressed air is generally prohibited as a cleaning method, unless the compressed air is used in conjunction with a ventilation system that is designed to capture the airborne dust created by the compressed air. All persons doing the cleanup should be provided with suitable respiratory protection and personal protective clothing to prevent contact with lead.

The OSHA construction standard for lead requires that a competent person perform frequent and regular inspections of jobsites, materials, and equipment. A competent person is defined by the standard as one who is capable of identifying existing and predictable lead hazards and who has the authority to take prompt corrective measures to eliminate them.

Presently, in the construction industry, respirators must often be used to supplement engineering controls and work practices. To provide adequate respiratory protection, respirators must be donned before entering the work area and should not be removed until the worker has left the area, or as part of a decontamination procedure. Employers must assure that the respirator issued to the employee is properly selected and properly fitted so that it exhibits minimum face piece leakage. **The employer—at no cost to employees—must supply respirators.** Employers must perform either qualitative or quantitative fit tests for each employee wearing negative pressure respirators. Fit testing is to be performed at the time of the initial fitting and at least semiannually thereafter.

OSHA has developed a computer program, *Lead in Construction Advisor 1.0* (available from their web-site) to help users understand the standard. The program is NOT a substitute for the standard, but a valuable tool to be used with it.

This interactive software program provides an introduction to the scope and logic of the regulation, as well as a summary to facilitate compliance. The program requests information about the work place policies, activities, and exposures in order to offer guidance on how the standard might apply to your situation. This can be very useful in helping you determine if there is a problem and, if so, its severity.

PROJECTS INVOLVING LEAD RENOVATION

A federal lead based paint regulation, the Lead Pre-Renovation Education Rule (Lead PRE), became effective on June 1, 1999. This regulation requires a contractor to distribute the EPA pamphlet "Protect Your Family From Lead In Your Home" before beginning renovations in housing built before 1978 in which more that two square feet of painted surfaces will be disturbed. The contractor is required to provide the EPA pamphlet to the owner and an adult occupant of the structure and obtain a written acknowledgement of receipt, or mail the pamphlet by certified mail seven days prior to starting work. In multi-family housing, each tenant needs to be provided with the pamphlet, information about the availability of additional pamphlets, as well as the nature, location, and timing of the renovation. Notification records must be kept for a minimum of three years.

For the purposes of this rule the EPA has made the following distinction between abatement and renovation:

◊ Abatement means work that is designed to **permanently** eliminate lead based paint hazards, including the removal of lead contaminated dust and the covering or removal of lead contaminated soil. Included are projects where a written contract or other documentation provides that an individual or firm certified in accordance with EPA regulations will be doing the work.

◊ Renovation work consists of **repairing, restoring, or remodeling** projects that are not designed to permanently eliminate the hazard of lead based paint in a structure, even though these activities may result in the reduction or elimination of lead based paint hazards. It includes the modification or removal of any part of a structure that disturbs painted surfaces, surface preparation (sanding, scraping, or creating any paint dust), and window replacement.

Exclusions to the rule include the following:

◊ Emergency repairs that pose little likelihood of creating lead hazards;

◊ Minor maintenance and repairs that disturb less than two square feet of painted surfaces;

◊ Housing declared lead-free by a certified lead inspector; and

◊ Zero-bedroom housing.

It is unlawful to fail or refuse to comply with the regulations. Violators may be subject to a civil penalty of up to $25,000 per day for each violation. Criminal fines of up to $25,000 per day and imprisonment for up to one year may be imposed for knowingly or willfully violating the provisions of the rule.

Additional information on the Lead PRE program is available at **www.epa.gov/lead** or by calling 1-800-424-lead.

OSHA's Form 300 (Rev. 01/2004)

Log of Work-Related Injuries and Illnesses

You must record information about every work-related death and about every work-related injury or illness that involves loss of consciousness, restricted work activity or job transfer, days away from work, or medical treatment beyond first aid. You must also record significant work-related injuries and illnesses that are diagnosed by a physician or licensed health care professional. You must also record work-related injuries and illnesses that meet any of the specific recording criteria listed in 29 CFR Part 1904.8 through 1904.12. Feel free to use two lines for a single case if you need to. You must complete an Injury and Illness Incident Report (OSHA Form 301) or equivalent form for each injury or illness recorded on this form. If you're not sure whether a case is recordable, call your local OSHA office for help.

Year 20 ____

U.S. Department of Labor
Occupational Safety and Health Administration

Form approved OMB no. 1218-0176

Establishment name _____

City _____ State _____

Identify the person

(A) Case no.	(B) Employee's name	(C) Job title (e.g., Welder)

Describe the case

(D) Date of injury or onset of illness	(E) Where the event occurred (e.g., Loading dock north end)	(F) Describe injury or illness, parts of body affected, and object/substance that directly injured or made person ill (e.g., Second degree burns on right forearm from acetylene torch)
___/___ month/day		
___/___ month/day		
___/___ month/day		
___/___ month/day		
___/___ month/day		
___/___ month/day		
___/___ month/day		
___/___ month/day		
___/___ month/day		
___/___ month/day		
___/___ month/day		
___/___ month/day		
___/___ month/day		

Classify the case

CHECK ONLY ONE box for each case based on the most serious outcome for that case:

Death (G)	Days away from work (H)	Remained at Work — Job transfer or restriction (I)	Remained at Work — Other recordable cases (J)
☐	☐	☐	☐
☐	☐	☐	☐
☐	☐	☐	☐
☐	☐	☐	☐
☐	☐	☐	☐
☐	☐	☐	☐
☐	☐	☐	☐
☐	☐	☐	☐
☐	☐	☐	☐
☐	☐	☐	☐
☐	☐	☐	☐
☐	☐	☐	☐
☐	☐	☐	☐

Enter the number of days the injured or ill worker was:

Away from work (K)	On job transfer or restriction (L)
_____ days	_____ days
_____ days	_____ days
_____ days	_____ days
_____ days	_____ days
_____ days	_____ days
_____ days	_____ days
_____ days	_____ days
_____ days	_____ days
_____ days	_____ days
_____ days	_____ days
_____ days	_____ days
_____ days	_____ days
_____ days	_____ days

Check the "Injury" column or choose one type of illness:

(M) Injury (1)	Skin disorder (2)	Respiratory condition (3)	Poisoning (4)	Hearing loss (5)	All other illnesses (6)
☐	☐	☐	☐	☐	☐
☐	☐	☐	☐	☐	☐
☐	☐	☐	☐	☐	☐
☐	☐	☐	☐	☐	☐
☐	☐	☐	☐	☐	☐
☐	☐	☐	☐	☐	☐
☐	☐	☐	☐	☐	☐
☐	☐	☐	☐	☐	☐
☐	☐	☐	☐	☐	☐
☐	☐	☐	☐	☐	☐
☐	☐	☐	☐	☐	☐
☐	☐	☐	☐	☐	☐
☐	☐	☐	☐	☐	☐

Page totals ▶

Be sure to transfer these totals to the Summary page (Form 300A) before you post it.

Injury (1)	Skin disorder (2)	Respiratory condition (3)	Poisoning (4)	Hearing loss (5)	All other illnesses (6)

Page ____ of ____

Public reporting burden for this collection of information is estimated to average 14 minutes per response, including time to review the instructions, search and gather the data needed, and complete and review the collection of information. Persons are not required to respond to the collection of information unless it displays a currently valid OMB control number. If you have any comments about these estimates or any other aspects of this data collection, contact: US Department of Labor, OSHA Office of Statistical Analysis, Room N-3644, 200 Constitution Avenue, NW, Washington, DC 20210. Do not send the completed forms to this office.

Summary of Work-Related Injuries and Illnesses

All establishments covered by Part 1904 must complete this Summary page, even if no work-related injuries or illnesses occurred during the year. Remember to review the Log to verify that the entries are complete and accurate before completing this summary.

Using the Log, count the individual entries you made for each category. Then write the totals below, making sure you've added the entries from every page of the Log. If you had no cases, write "0."

Employees, former employees, and their representatives have the right to review the OSHA Form 300 in its entirety. They also have limited access to the OSHA Form 301 or its equivalent. See 29 CFR Part 1904.35, in OSHA's recordkeeping rule, for further details on the access provisions for these forms.

Number of Cases

Total number of deaths	Total number of cases with days away from work	Total number of cases with job transfer or restriction	Total number of other recordable cases
_____ (G)	_____ (H)	_____ (I)	_____ (J)

Number of Days

Total number of days away from work	Total number of days of job transfer or restriction
_____ (K)	_____ (L)

Injury and Illness Types

Total number of . . .
(M)

(1) Injuries _____
(2) Skin disorders _____
(3) Respiratory conditions _____

(4) Poisonings _____
(5) Hearing loss _____
(6) All other illnesses _____

Post this Summary page from February 1 to April 30 of the year following the year covered by the form.

Public reporting burden for this collection of information is estimated to average 50 minutes per response, including time to review the instructions, search and gather the data needed, and complete and review the collection of information. Persons are not required to respond to the collection of information unless it displays a currently valid OMB control number. If you have any comments about these estimates or any other aspects of this data collection, contact: US Department of Labor, OSHA Office of Statistical Analysis, Room N-3644, 200 Constitution Avenue, NW, Washington, DC 20210. Do not send the completed forms to this office.

Establishment information

Your establishment name _____

Street _____

City _____ State ____ ZIP ____

Industry description (e.g., Manufacture of motor truck trailers) _____

Standard Industrial Classification (SIC), if known (e.g., 3715) _____

OR

North American Industrial Classification (NAICS), if known (e.g., 336212) _____

Employment information (If you don't have these figures, see the Worksheet on the back of this page to estimate.)

Annual average number of employees _____

Total hours worked by all employees last year _____

Sign here

Knowingly falsifying this document may result in a fine.

I certify that I have examined this document and that to the best of my knowledge the entries are true, accurate, and complete.

_____   _____
Company executive   Title

_____   ____/____/____
Phone   Date

U.S. Department of Labor
Occupational Safety and Health Administration

Form approved OMB no. 1218-0176

OSHA's Form 301
Injury and Illness Incident Report

Attention: This form contains information relating to employee health and must be used in a manner that protects the confidentiality of employees to the extent possible while the information is being used for occupational safety and health purposes.

This *Injury and Illness Incident Report* is one of the first forms you must fill out when a recordable work-related injury or illness has occurred. Together with the *Log of Work-Related Injuries and Illnesses* and the accompanying *Summary*, these forms help the employer and OSHA develop a picture of the extent and severity of work-related incidents.

Within 7 calendar days after you receive information that a recordable work-related injury or illness has occurred, you must fill out this form or an equivalent. Some state workers' compensation, insurance, or other reports may be acceptable substitutes. To be considered an equivalent form, any substitute must contain all the information asked for on this form.

According to Public Law 91-596 and 29 CFR 1904, OSHA's recordkeeping rule, you must keep this form on file for 5 years following the year to which it pertains.

If you need additional copies of this form, you may photocopy and use as many as you need.

Completed by _____

Title _____

Phone (_____) _____ – _____   Date ___ / ___ / ___

Information about the employee

1) Full name _____

2) Street _____

   City _____ State _____ ZIP _____

3) Date of birth ___ / ___ / ___

4) Date hired ___ / ___ / ___

5) ☐ Male
   ☐ Female

Information about the physician or other health care professional

6) Name of physician or other health care professional _____

7) If treatment was given away from the worksite, where was it given?

   Facility _____

   Street _____

   City _____ State _____ ZIP _____

8) Was employee treated in an emergency room?
   ☐ Yes
   ☐ No

9) Was employee hospitalized overnight as an in-patient?
   ☐ Yes
   ☐ No

Information about the case

10) Case number from the Log _____ *(Transfer the case number from the Log after you record the case.)*

11) Date of injury or illness ___ / ___ / ___

12) Time employee began work _____ AM / PM

13) Time of event _____ AM / PM ☐ Check if time cannot be determined

14) **What was the employee doing just before the incident occurred?** Describe the activity, as well as the tools, equipment, or material the employee was using. Be specific. *Examples:* "climbing a ladder while carrying roofing materials"; "spraying chlorine from hand sprayer"; "daily computer key-entry."

15) **What happened?** Tell us how the injury occurred. *Examples:* "When ladder slipped on wet floor, worker fell 20 feet"; "Worker was sprayed with chlorine when gasket broke during replacement"; "Worker developed soreness in wrist over time."

16) **What was the injury or illness?** Tell us the part of the body that was affected and how it was affected; be more specific than "hurt," "pain," or sore." *Examples:* "strained back"; "chemical burn, hand"; "carpal tunnel syndrome."

17) **What object or substance directly harmed the employee?** *Examples:* "concrete floor"; "chlorine"; "radial arm saw." *If this question does not apply to the incident, leave it blank.*

18) **If the employee died, when did death occur?** Date of death ___ / ___ / ___

Public reporting burden for this collection of information is estimated to average 22 minutes per response, including time for reviewing instructions, searching existing data sources, gathering and maintaining the data needed, and completing and reviewing the collection of information. Persons are not required to respond to the collection of information unless it displays a current valid OMB control number. If you have any comments about this estimate or any other aspects of this data collection, including suggestions for reducing this burden, contact: US Department of Labor, OSHA Office of Statistics, Room N-3644, 200 Constitution Avenue, NW, Washington, DC 20210. Do not send the completed forms to this office.

CHAPTER 7
EMPLOYER OBLIGATIONS

Numerous federal and state laws govern the way business is conducted. Many of these laws deal directly with the relationship between the employer and the employees.

Some of the more important regulations are discussed in the paragraphs that follow. This information is provided as a general guide. Complete copies of the laws and regulations are generally available for free from public libraries and government offices.

FAIR LABOR STANDARDS ACT

The Fair Labor Standards Act (FLSA) establishes minimum wage, overtime pay for work exceeding 40 hours per week, record keeping, and child labor standards affecting full and part time workers in the government (federal, state, local) and the private sector. The Act also provides definitions and rules for employees known commonly as exempt (non-hourly) or non-exempt (hourly) employees. **The Act applies to all employers who have one or more employees.**

The act requires employers to pay the minimum wage ($5.15 per hour as of 9/1/97) to all covered and non-exempt employees for all hours physically worked. The act also requires overtime payment of at least one and one-half times (1½) an employee's regular hourly rate of pay for all covered and non-exempt employees for all hours over 40 worked in any workweek. The regular rate of pay includes basic pay plus non-discretionary bonuses, shift premiums, and production bonuses.

Overtime is paid on time physically worked, not time compensated. Overtime is not required to be paid for sick, holiday, and vacation time or for any day not physically worked. For example, if an employee has a paid 8-hour holiday, vacation, or sick day in a workweek and in the same workweek also works 40 hours, the employee would receive 48 hours of straight time, not 40 hours of straight time and 8 hours of overtime.

It is important to note that employees and employers may not enter into any agreement that violates the provisions of the Fair Labor Standards Act, as it relates to the payment of overtime for time worked. Also, state laws may impose additional requirements for the payment of overtime. A check of state laws is necessary to ensure full compliance with the laws.

Additionally, employers are required to comply with the Fair Labor Standards Act's child labor standards. These standards are designed to protect the educational opportunities of minors and prohibit oppressive child labor, which is defined as the employment of children under the age of 16. Note that children between the ages of 14 and 16 may be employed in non-hazardous conditions that do not interfere with their schooling, health, and well-being. The minimum age for employment in hazardous occupations is 18. It is probably safe to say that children under the age of 18 should never be hired in the construction business, unless it is for office work.

Also, the act requires employers to keep on file, for review and inspection by the Department of Labor, accurate time sheets that show the hours worked each day and each workweek for non-exempt employees, as well as historical records of hourly wages and total wages paid. For the purposes of the Act, a workweek is defined as a period of 168 hours during 7 consecutive 24-hour periods. A workweek may begin on any day of the week and at any hour established by the employer. In general, each workweek stands alone for the purposes of minimum wage and overtime payment.

The act does not require employers to provide vacation, holiday, severance, or sick pay. Nor does it require lunch breaks, rest periods, holidays, or vacations. Additionally, the Act does not require premium pay for weekend or holiday work and does not require employers to give pay raises or fringe benefits. While these matters are generally for agreement between employers and employees, it is prudent to check the requirements of the state where the business is located and to assess what the competitors provide for their employees. Additionally, the Act does not limit the number of hours in a day or days in a week an employee may be required or scheduled to work, including overtime hours, provided the employee is at least 16 years of age.

Exempt Employees

Exempt employees, that is those who are exempted from the rules regarding the payment of overtime, are those whose job duties usually fall into the following categories:

◊ Professional

◊ Administrative

◊ Outside Salespeople

◊ Executive/Management

In addition to the exempt employees noted, there are two key exceptions to the provisions of the Fair Labor Standards Act. Those are:

1) employees who are legally exempt from coverage, such as certain farm workers, full-time students, apprentices, handicapped workers, and those in some specialized or seasonal employment, and

2) independent contractors or contract employees.

The difference between employees and independent contractors, or contract employees, is not always obvious. In general, persons working as independent contractors need to meet the following criteria:

◊ Ability to set their own hours of work and determine the sequence of work;

◊ Work by the project rather than having a continuous relationship with the employer;

◊ Are paid by the job;

◊ Have an opportunity for profit and loss; that is they run their own business; and

◊ Furnish their own tools and training.

Additionally, working with a company that leases employees is regarded as contract employment and is exempt from the FLSA.

Willful violations of the Fair Labor Standards Act or the related child labor provisions are subject to criminal and civil prosecution with fines of up to $10,000. A second violation may result in a prison term. Employers who willfully or repeatedly violate the minimum wage or overtime pay requirements are subject to civil money penalties of up to $1,000 for each violation.

Non-Exempt Employees

Non-Exempt employees, that is those who are governed by the FLSA, are those who are customarily associated with the following categories:

◊ Clerical - receptionist, file clerk;

◊ Maintenance - drivers, custodians;

◊ Production Lines - laborers, craftsmen;

◊   Services - cleaning crews, window washers; or

◊   Paraprofessional.

A more recent addition to the FLSA, the Equal Pay Act of 1963, passed by congressional amendment, requires equal pay for equal work without regard to the sex of the employee. In essence, this provision of the law requires the employer to pay the same pay for the same work to both men and women. There may be pay differences due to longevity or to skill, but these must be clearly and plainly documented.

THE ADA

The Americans with Disabilities Act (ADA) was passed in 1990. This is a civil rights law that prohibits employers from discriminating against qualified people with disabilities by refusing to hire or promote those people because of their disabilities. **The law applies to all employers who have 15 or more employees.**

Other provisions of the act prohibit discrimination in transportation, public accommodations, public services, and telecommunications services. Businesses generally deal with the provisions of this act that relate to the hiring of employees.

The disabilities covered by the ADA include substantial impairments to daily living that limit the following life functions:

◊   seeing,

◊   hearing,

◊   walking,

◊   breathing,

◊   learning,

◊   working,

◊   self-care, and

◊   manual tasks.

It is important to remember that the Act covers individuals with disabilities who have a physical or mental impairment that substantially limits one or more major life activities. This includes impairments such as epilepsy, paralysis, mental retardation, and significant hearing losses. The Act also covers AIDS, HIV diseases, and other communicable diseases. Alcoholism and drug addiction are also covered, if related to a previous condition for which the employee is undergoing therapy or treatment.

If an applicant meets the legitimate skill, experience, education, or other requirements of a job, *the employer may not discriminate in hiring because of a disability.* The law does not cover individuals with non-chronic conditions, such as a broken arm or a severe cold.

IMMIGRATION REFORM AND CONTROL ACT (IRCA)

In 1986, Congress enacted a reform to the Immigration and Naturalization Act. Employers must now ensure that all persons hired are either legal citizens or registered non-citizens. In order to comply with that act, a completed I-9 Form must be obtained from all new employees within three days of hire. **This law applies to all employers of one or more employees.**

The I-9 Form requires that employees present evidence of their citizenship or legal status by presenting a single document that establishes identity and employment eligibility.

Only the following single documents are acceptable:

◊   United States passport,

◊   certificate of U.S. citizenship,

◊   certificate of naturalization,

◊   resident alien registration card with photo ID, or

◊   current foreign passport with employment authorization.

Identity and employment eligibility may also be established by presenting one identity document, such as a:

◊   state-issued driver license with photo,

◊   U.S. military card, or

◊   Government ID card.

The employee must also then present one employment eligibility document, such as:

◊   an original Social Security card,

◊   a U.S. birth certificate,

◊   a current INS employment authorization,

◊   Reentry permit, or

◊   Native American and Tribal documents.

**WORKERS'
COMPENSATION
INSURANCE**

The Federal Workers' Compensation Law was the first insurance of its kind to develop widely in the United States to protect the income of employees disabled by work-related illness or injury. While limited in its original scope, the law, with its associated state-established programs, covers a broad range of occupational injuries and diseases attributable to work related accidents and now also covers occupational diseases. Programs covering occupational disease are limited in many States by time limitations for the filing of claims.

In general, virtually every hourly and salaried employee is covered under federal and state laws, with exceptions granted in most states for domestic service, agriculture, and casual labor. Many programs exempt employees of charitable and religious institutions and a few limit coverage only to workers in hazardous situations. A very few states allow employers to reject coverage under the law; however, in so doing, employers in these states also lose certain protections against lawsuits brought by employees injured on the job.

Benefits provided under workers' compensation insurance include weekly payments to injured and temporarily disabled employees in amounts ranging from 66 2/3% to 80% of gross wages to a prescribed maximum. Additionally, benefits include the payment of medical bills incurred as a result of the injury and, in the unfortunate case of death as a result of a work accident, death and funeral benefits are paid to the survivors. In cases of permanent disability, most programs provide for a lump sum payment and also provide benefits for retraining of injured employees in new occupations.

Workers' compensation is totally funded by employer contributions and can be a significant cost of doing business. Employers pay a percentage rate for the insurance based on every $100 unit of payroll covered to a maximum payroll dollar per employee. The rate is based on several factors, including the nature of the business; the hazards likely in the business, the frequency of accidents and injuries, and the severity (translated as cost) of the accident, injury, or death.

Workers' compensation insurance, like many other insurances, operates in a very competitive market. Compensation carriers, that is companies that sell workers' compensation insurance, are always developing new ways to reduce compensation costs through the identification and management of workplace risk factors. Many companies will assist employers in developing safety programs, drug-screening programs, and risk management programs; all designed to reduce the occurrence of accident and injury on the job. Considering that workers' compensation insurance can cost up to 2% of covered payroll, it is a wise employer who works closely with the workers' compensation insurance carrier to reduce work related injuries and, in the process, the cost of workers' compensation insurance.

UNEMPLOYMENT COMPENSATION

Unemployment insurance is a form of temporary compensation to workers who have lost their jobs through layoffs or reasons that are not related to job performance. The compensation provided is usually a percentage of the employee's previous wages to a prescribed maximum. In most cases, compensation is provided until the employee finds a new job or for a defined time period, whichever is shorter.

Both the federal and state governments share in the administration of unemployment programs, with much of the federal program administered through the Federal Unemployment Tax Act (FUTA). States administer their specific unemployment programs under FUTA standards and as approved by the Secretary of Labor. Check the unemployment rules and regulations in your state to ensure that you are in full compliance with both state and federal regulations.

The support for unemployment compensation comes from employers, who pay federal and state unemployment taxes based on the amount of wages paid; the amount contributed to the state and federal unemployment fund; and the amount paid from the funds to their employees who have been laid off or otherwise have their employment terminated.

CHILD SUPPORT ENFORCEMENT

The Personal Responsibility and Work Opportunity Reconciliation Act (PRWORA) of 1996 requires employers to report certain information on all new hires to the state agency designated to enforce child support laws. The information reported is matched to a state database to determine if the new hire has a child support obligation through an existing support order. The review is also able to establish whether or not the new hire is living up to his or her child support obligation. Since 30% of all child support obligations cross state lines, the state data is forwarded to the National Directory of New Hires for a similar check.

Frequency of employer reporting is based primarily on the number of employees and the number of new hires. In most cases, the minimum reporting requirement is once every two months. The reporting is done on a standardized form and is not difficult or time-consuming, as the information reported is readily gathered in the application process.

OTHER FEDERAL ACTS

Other major labor regulations that may have an impact on construction employers include the following (unless indicated otherwise, the provisions apply to employers of one or more employees).

COBRA

While federal law does not require employers to provide health care benefits to their employees, employers who do provide coverage must allow for continuation of the coverage when employees or family members have a qualifying event.

A qualifying event for an employee is the voluntary or involuntary termination of employment, other than for gross misconduct. Terminated employees may continue their health insurance coverage for up to 18 months at their expense.

Qualifying events for family members include:

◊ Death of the employee,

◊ Divorce,

◊ Coverage loss, as a result of Medicaid eligibility,

◊ A dependent child becoming ineligible under the plan, or

◊ Loss of coverage following the bankruptcy of a retired employee's employer.

The provisions of the Consolidated Omnibus Reconciliation Act (COBRA) that relate to employee benefits may impact the business. While the primary issue is the continuation of medical insurance benefits for prior employees, COBRA has been somewhat confusing and problematic for employers. Most of the COBRA complaints concern inadequate or improper notification of available COBRA benefits. It is strongly suggested that diligent adherence to the information and notification requirements be observed.

Employer Polygraph Protection Act

This law bars most employers from using lie detectors on employees. There are a few narrowly defined positions for security sensitive positions; however, it is unlikely that any of these positions fall within the construction trades. The law is administered by the Wage and Hour Division of the Employment Standards Administration of the Department of Labor.

Wage Garnishment Law

The Wage Garnishment Law limits the amount of pay that can be taken under a garnishment order. It protects employees to some extent from firing due to garnishment. Usually this is 25% of disposable income, 15% per week, if the person is head of a family. Disposable income is net pay remaining following the deduction of any amounts required by law. The 25% and 15% limitations do not apply to court ordered child support, Chapter XIII Bankruptcy, and debt for federal or state taxes.

Uniformed Services Employment Act

Certain persons in the armed forces have a right to re-employment with the employer they were with when they entered the service. This includes those called up from the reserves or National Guard. The Veteran's Employment and Training Service administers these rules. **This law applies to employers of one or more employees.**

Title VII of the Civil Rights Act, Equal Employment Opportunity Act

Title VII of the Civil Rights Act of 1964 and the Equal Employment Opportunity Act of 1972 apply **to employers of 15 or more people**. These laws prohibit discrimination, or less favorable treatment, in employment based on race, color, religion, sex, or national origin. The Civil Rights Act of 1991 also provides for compensatory and punitive damages in cases of intentional discrimination.

Family and Medical Leave Act

The Family and Medical Leave Act of 1993 entitles eligible employees to take unpaid leave for medical reasons; the birth or adoption of a child; and for the care of a child, spouse, or parent with a serious health condition. It applies to both male and female employees and is **a requirement of any employer of 50 or more employees**.

Labor Organizing, Bargaining, and Dispute Resolution Acts

Various labor organizing, bargaining, and dispute resolution acts from 1932 to 1959 may impact contractors. They include the following, which are **required of employers with one or more employees:**

◊ Norris La Guardia Act of 1932 gives labor the right to organize and strike under federal law, while at the same time restricting the issuance of labor injunctions in labor disputes.

◊ National Labor Relations Act of 1935 guaranteed covered workers the right to organize and join labor movement and to bargain collectively through representatives.

◊ Taft-Hartley Act of 1947 retained the workers basic right to join unions, bargain collectively, and strike.

◊ Landrum-Griffin Act of 1959 defined unfair labor practices, banned organizational picketing, and allowed state agencies to assume jurisdiction over labor disputes declined by the NLRB.

Age Discrimination in Employment Act

The Age Discrimination in Employment Act protects employees aged 40 to 65 from discrimination in firms of 20 or more employees. It mandates equal treatment, rather than preferential or discriminatory treatment, for older workers.

Right to Work Laws

"Right to Work" laws, existing in 21 states as of December 2000, ensure the rights of an employee to decide whether or not to join or to otherwise financially support a union. Before relying on the text of any state "Right to Work" statute, check the most recent edition of the state law and/or consult with an attorney.

PERSONNEL FILES

Employee personnel files contain all the pertinent information on the firm's employees. At a minimum, the employee personnel file should contain the following documents and information, and be maintained for at least 4 years.

Application and Hire Record

This document should include the name, address, and phone number of the applicant, references, and a record of any previous employment. If the applicant is hired, the hire record portions are completed and contain the date hired, standard and overtime rates, benefits, and emergency contacts.

Medical Information

This section should be maintained as a separate section of the file to comply with recent rulings regarding the confidentiality of employee medical records. It includes information about an employee's physicals, health claims, and other related medical information.

Wage/Salary Section

This file contains the federal W-4 withholding information form, the I-9 immigration form, and any state or local income tax election documents. A Form W-4 remains in effect until the employee provides a new one. If a new employee does not provide a completed W-4, withholding is determined as if the employee is single with no withholding allowances. W-4s claiming more than ten withholding allowances or an exemption from withholding where wages will normally be over $200 per week must be sent to the IRS at the end of the quarter in which they were received. Employees not claiming exempt status, but not earning enough to require income tax withholding, must be notified that they may be eligible to claim a tax refund due to the Earned Income Credit (EIC).

The employee personnel files may take any form or design and may be as inclusive or exclusive as the employer wishes, provided, at a minimum, the items noted above are collected and maintained. Very often, local stationery stores have pre-made designs and forms that make maintaining a complete personnel file a straightforward process.

RECORD KEEPING

Laws, rules, and regulations regarding time cards, payroll taxes, deductions, and other record keeping requirements will make it seem like running a separate personnel agency, in addition to conducting the regular business. Increased regulatory requirements make the maintenance of accurate payroll and deduction information mandatory, as fines for failure to properly file or to pay on time can be extremely high.

In addition to the details contained in the employee's personnel file, the following payroll information should also be retained:

◊ Amounts and dates of all wage, annuity and pension payments;

◊ The amount of any reported or allocated tips;

◊ The fair market value of in-kind wages;

◊ Employee copies of returned Form W-2;

◊ The amount and periods for which employees were paid for absences due to sickness or injury;

◊ The dates and amounts of tax deposits;

◊ Copies of returns filed; and

◊ A record of fringe benefits provided.

RECORDING HOURS WORKED

The Fair Labor Standards Act, as amended, states in part that "accurate and complete records of employee work hours must be maintained". Nothing could be more significant to avoid trouble with the IRS, the Federal Labor Board, or the local labor board.

There are several ways to maintain accurate and complete hours worked for employees. Among these are the following:

◊ automated punch clock,

◊ magnetic strip readers, and

◊ hand-written time sheets.

Two things to consider, before using any system, are cost and the number of employees. Mechanized systems are often cost prohibitive for smaller businesses. Most employers rely on a manual timecard system. On a daily basis, the employee physically records on the card his or her hours worked, noting the start and stop time of each workday, and the hours worked are recorded weekly.

Time card records must not only be accurate, but they must also be signed. They must be maintained for at least four years in case of disputes with employees or the dreaded IRS audit.

INFORMATION RETURNS

Previously, in the section on the Fair Labor Standards Act, the difference between employees and independent contractors was discussed. Wages paid to employees are subject to withholding requirements, social security, and Medicare tax while amounts paid to independent contractors are not. Employee wages are reported on Form W-2 and amounts exceeding $600 paid to independent contractors are reported on Form 1099.

If an employee is improperly treated as an independent contractor, the employer may become liable for social security, Medicare, and income tax **not** withheld.

Form SS-8 (Determination of Worker Status for Purposes of Federal Employment Taxes and Income Tax withholding) may be filed with the IRS to request a determination as to whether a worker is an employee or independent contractor.

PREPARING A PAYROLL

Payroll systems, both manual and electronic, are available. Their cost and complexity depends on the business size and needs. Regardless of whether a manual or electronic system is used, the system must account for the following:

◊   federal withholding taxes,

◊   state withholding, if applicable,

◊   FICA (Social Security tax),

◊   Medicare tax,

◊   FUTA (unemployment tax),

◊   SUI (state unemployment insurance),

◊   employee benefits (if any),

◊   workers' compensation coverage, and

◊   miscellaneous deductions (such as union dues or health insurance).

The following steps should be followed in preparing a payroll for each employee:

◊   Calculate the gross pay from the time sheet and rate of pay with any adjustment for overtime, if at a different rate.

◊   Withhold federal income tax based on the employee's Form W-4 (see partial table on page 7-15).

◊   Withhold the employee's share of social security tax (6.2% of gross pay to $90,000 in 2005).

◊   Withhold the employee's share of Medicare tax (1.45% of gross pay without limit).

◊   Include advance earned income credit, if requested on Form W-5.

◊   Withhold state income taxes, if applicable.

◊   Withhold any miscellaneous deductions authorized by the employee.

Special rules may apply to children or spouses who are employees in a family business. Generally, the rules may exempt social security, Medicare, and FUTA taxes for children under 21 and FUTA taxes for spouses under certain circumstances.

The net paycheck given to the employee should include a statement showing the calculation of gross pay and the detail of all deductions.

Employers are responsible for a matching share of social security and Medicare taxes, as well as federal unemployment (FUTA), state unemployment (SUI) and worker's compensation insurance. The cost of these items may not be deducted from an employee's pay.

The FUTA (Federal Unemployment Tax) applies to the first $7,000 of an employee's wages each year. The FUTA tax rate is 6.2%, however, a credit of 5.4% is allowed for the timely payment of state unemployment taxes, regardless of the amount (net rate of .8%). The state rate may vary depending on the company's history of unemployment claims and may be subject to a higher taxable wage base.

MARRIED Persons—WEEKLY Payroll Period
(For Wages Paid 2005)

At Least	But less than	0	1	2	3	4	5	6	7	8	9	10
$0	$125	$0	$0	$0	$0	$0	$0	$0	$0	$0	$0	$0
125	130	0	0	0	0	0	0	0	0	0	0	0
130	135	0	0	0	0	0	0	0	0	0	0	0
135	140	0	0	0	0	0	0	0	0	0	0	0
140	145	0	0	0	0	0	0	0	0	0	0	0
145	150	0	0	0	0	0	0	0	0	0	0	0
150	155	0	0	0	0	0	0	0	0	0	0	0
155	160	0	0	0	0	0	0	0	0	0	0	0
160	165	1	0	0	0	0	0	0	0	0	0	0
165	170	1	0	0	0	0	0	0	0	0	0	0
170	175	2	0	0	0	0	0	0	0	0	0	0
175	180	2	0	0	0	0	0	0	0	0	0	0
180	185	3	0	0	0	0	0	0	0	0	0	0
185	190	3	0	0	0	0	0	0	0	0	0	0
190	195	4	0	0	0	0	0	0	0	0	0	0
195	200	4	0	0	0	0	0	0	0	0	0	0
200	210	5	0	0	0	0	0	0	0	0	0	0
210	220	6	0	0	0	0	0	0	0	0	0	0
220	230	7	1	0	0	0	0	0	0	0	0	0
230	240	8	2	0	0	0	0	0	0	0	0	0
240	250	9	3	0	0	0	0	0	0	0	0	0
250	260	10	4	0	0	0	0	0	0	0	0	0
260	270	11	5	0	0	0	0	0	0	0	0	0
270	280	12	6	0	0	0	0	0	0	0	0	0
280	290	13	7	1	0	0	0	0	0	0	0	0
290	300	14	8	2	0	0	0	0	0	0	0	0
300	310	15	9	3	0	0	0	0	0	0	0	0
310	320	16	10	4	0	0	0	0	0	0	0	0
320	330	17	11	5	0	0	0	0	0	0	0	0
330	340	18	12	6	0	0	0	0	0	0	0	0
340	350	19	13	7	1	0	0	0	0	0	0	0
350	360	20	14	8	2	0	0	0	0	0	0	0
360	370	21	15	9	3	0	0	0	0	0	0	0
370	380	22	16	10	4	0	0	0	0	0	0	0
380	390	23	17	11	5	0	0	0	0	0	0	0
390	400	24	18	12	6	0	0	0	0	0	0	0
400	410	25	19	13	7	1	0	0	0	0	0	0
410	420	26	20	14	8	2	0	0	0	0	0	0
420	430	27	21	15	9	3	0	0	0	0	0	0
430	440	28	22	16	10	4	0	0	0	0	0	0
440	450	30	23	17	11	5	0	0	0	0	0	0
450	460	31	24	18	12	6	0	0	0	0	0	0
460	470	33	25	19	13	7	0	0	0	0	0	0
470	480	34	26	20	14	8	1	0	0	0	0	0
480	490	36	27	21	15	9	2	0	0	0	0	0
490	500	37	28	22	16	10	3	0	0	0	0	0
500	510	39	29	23	17	11	4	0	0	0	0	0
510	520	40	31	24	18	12	5	0	0	0	0	0
520	530	42	32	25	19	13	6	0	0	0	0	0
530	540	43	34	26	20	14	7	1	0	0	0	0
540	550	45	35	27	21	15	8	2	0	0	0	0
550	560	46	37	28	22	16	9	3	0	0	0	0
560	570	48	38	29	23	17	10	4	0	0	0	0
570	580	49	40	31	24	18	11	5	0	0	0	0
580	590	51	41	32	25	19	12	6	0	0	0	0
590	600	52	43	34	26	20	13	7	1	0	0	0
600	610	54	44	35	27	21	14	8	2	0	0	0
610	620	55	46	37	28	22	15	9	3	0	0	0
620	630	57	47	38	29	23	16	10	4	0	0	0
630	640	58	49	40	30	24	17	11	5	0	0	0
640	650	60	50	41	32	25	18	12	6	0	0	0
650	660	61	52	43	33	26	19	13	7	1	0	0
660	670	63	53	44	35	27	20	14	8	2	0	0
670	680	64	55	46	36	28	21	15	9	3	0	0
680	690	66	56	47	38	29	22	16	10	4	0	0

PAYROLL REPORTS AND PAYMENT OF TAXES

Once the various taxes have been withheld from the employees' paychecks, it is important to make sure that the money goes to the appropriate agency by the required method and in a timely manner.

IRS Publication 15 (Circular E, Employer's Tax Guide) covers all of the federal payroll reporting and depositing requirements.

The frequency of federal payroll tax payments depends on the amount of the accumulated tax liability and the payment history of the employer. Federal tax deposit requirements can be monthly, semiweekly, or within one banking day, depending on the size of the deposit.

◊ For employers with a history of $50,000 or less in deposits in the four prior July to June quarters, there are monthly deposit rules. Deposits are due on the 15th day of the following month. When the 15th lands on a holiday or weekend, the deposit is due on the next banking day. New businesses deposit on the monthly schedule, unless a daily requirement exist.

◊ A semiweekly deposit is required if the employer's prior July to June deposit total exceeded $50,000. Deposits for payrolls made on Wednesday, Thursday, or Friday are due by the following Wednesday. Saturday, Sunday, and Monday payrolls require a deposit by the following Friday.

◊ Employers with an accumulated liability of $100,000 must deposit within one banking day of the payroll check date. If a monthly depositor becomes subject to the one-day rule, the employer automatically becomes a semiweekly depositor.

Employers with an accumulated liability of less than $2,500 for the quarter may deposit the taxes or remit the amount with the form 941 Quarterly Employer's Tax Return by the due date of the return.

The method used to remit federal payroll taxes depends on the type and amount of tax involved. Methods include:

◊ Including payment with the quarterly Form 941, if the tax liability is less than $2,500. An FUTA accumulated liability of less than $500 can also be remitted with the annual Form 940 filing.

◊ Depositing the taxes with a bank qualified to accept federal tax payments, together with a Form 8109 Federal Tax Deposit Coupon.

◊ Using the Electronic Federal Tax Payment System (EFTPS), employers exceeding $200,000 in tax deposits, in a given year, must make electronic deposits beginning in the 2nd year after reaching this liability level. For example, those exceeding the $200,000 limit in 2002 will be required to make EFTPS deposits starting in 2004. Once the requirement is met to use the EFTPS method, Form 8109 deposits cannot be used, even if deposits fall below the threshold amount.

Deposits must be timely or the employer may face severe penalties. As the withheld funds are held in trust for the employees, they must be set aside and not used for any other purpose, other than for the purpose intended. Failure to remit or misapply the payroll taxes can result in penalties up to 100%! The following list of penalties may apply if required deposits are not made on time, if for less than the required amount, or if there is failure to use the EFTPS when required.

Deposit made one to five days late	2%
Deposit made six to 15 days late	5%
Deposit made 16 or more days late	10%
Payment made within ten days of first IRS notice requesting tax	10%
Failure to use EFTPS when required	10%
Payments made ten days, or more, after first IRS notice requesting tax	15%
When notice and demand for immediate payment is received	15%
Trust Fund penalty for taxes not paid if these taxes cannot be immediately collected	100%

The following table shows the dates for filing of various tax reports and the deposit requirements for FICA, Federal withholding, and FUTA taxes to ensure that IRS deadlines are met. If any date falls on a holiday or weekend, use the next business day.

By January 31: • Furnish Form 1099 to non-employees • Furnish Form W-2 to employees • Deposit FUTA taxes for 4th quarter • File Form 940 or 940 EZ • File fourth quarter Form 941 **By February 15:** • Request new Form W-4 from employees claiming withholding exemption **By February 28:** • File forms 1099 and 1096 • File Forms W-2 and W-3 **By March 15:** • File Form 1120 if a Corporation • File Form 1120S if an S Corporation **By March 31** • File Electronic 1099, W-2 and 8027, if applicable	**By April 15:** • File Form 1040 with Schedule C, if a Sole Proprietorship • File Form 1065, if a Partnership **By April 30:** • Deposit FUTA taxes if over \$100 • File first quarter Form 941 **By July 31:** • Deposit FUTA taxes, if over \$100 • File second quarter Form 941 **By October 31:** • Deposit FUTA taxes if over \$100 • File third quarter Form 941 **On December 31:** • Form W-5 expires for advance EIC payments

If the tax or fiscal year is different than the calendar year, the dates for filing of some returns will be different. Consult a tax advisor for the specific due dates, for a given fiscal year.

State payroll reporting requirements vary by state, but in general, the employer will have to file the following:

◊ withholding tax reports on a quarterly and annual basis;

◊ quarterly state unemployment tax reports; and

◊ workers' compensation insurance reports.

The payroll process, including recording of time, calculation of wages, preparation of checks, deposit of federal and state taxes, and record keeping, is one that lends itself to automation. Many payroll computer programs also have direct deposit features through the Internet, which will save time, money, and aggravation in handling the deposits of payroll taxes. There are numerous low priced computer software programs that can be used to process payroll, or as an alternative, an outside payroll service may provide this function. We suggest that either of these is a better alternative to a manual payroll system.

CHAPTER 8
FINANCIAL MANAGEMENT

This chapter will provide an overview of the basic accounting information necessary for a contractor to conduct informed discussions with accountants, bankers, and bonding agents. More importantly, it will enhance your financial understanding, which is very important for success in the construction industry. This chapter does not include all the material necessary for a complete understanding of construction bookkeeping and accounting principles and procedures; entire books have been written on those topics.

THE ACCOUNTING SYSTEM

Bookkeeping is the first step in the accounting process. It is the procedure in which financial transactions are entered in journals as they occur, normally on a daily basis. The entries in the journals are added up, usually monthly, and the account totals are entered (or posted) to the general ledger. The summary of the accounts in the general ledger results in financial statements for the company.

This accounting "cycle" from source document to financial statement is illustrated on the following page. The components of this system are described below.

SOURCE DOCUMENTS

Source documents consist of check stubs, deposit slips, invoices, receipts, billings, purchase orders, time cards, and other basic documents. They are created when money is paid or received, debt incurred, or a receivable created. They are the first transaction in the bookkeeping process and provide the basis for the various journal entries.

JOURNALS

Journals are used to classify the source document transactions by type. For example, checks, petty cash, and out-of-pocket payments would be shown in the disbursements journal. Payments received on construction contracts would be reflected in a sales or cash receipts journal. The number and types of journals depend on several factors, including the firm's size, complexity of operations, number of accounting transactions, and the degree of detailed information desired. Systems range from a single, all-inclusive, two-column journal, in which all transactions are recorded and summarized, to books utilizing multiple journals.

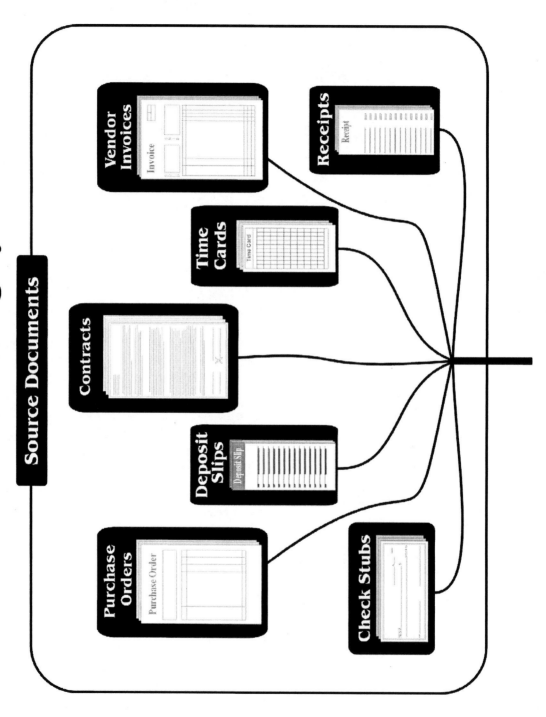

The Accounting Cycle

Source Documents

- Vendor Invoices
- Receipts
- Time Cards
- Contracts
- Deposit Slips
- Purchase Orders
- Check Stubs

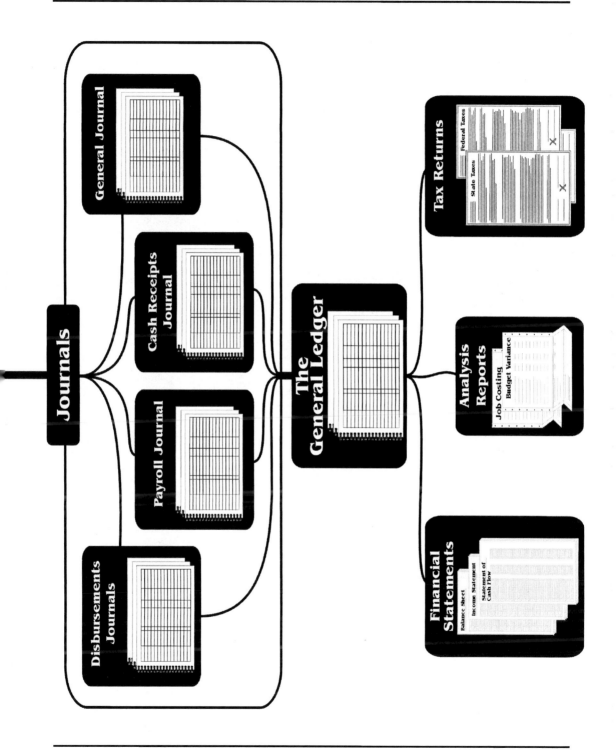

The journals shown in the illustrated accounting cycle are typical. They consist of the following items.

Payroll Journal

The *payroll journal* summarizes all of the employee wages. It provides the information necessary for various state and federal reports, some forms of liability insurance coverage, and workers' compensation reports. It also classifies employee wages for job costing purposes.

Disbursements Journal

The *disbursements journal* classifies amounts paid out by the nature of the expense. In larger, more active companies, a separate purchase or job cost journal may be set up to record material purchases and direct labor costs. On the other hand, in very small firms, it may be appropriate to combine the disbursements and payroll journals.

Sales/Cash Receipts Journal

The *sales/cash receipts journal* records all income. The information from this journal can be used for sales tax returns (when required) and job costing.

General Journal

The *general journal* records non-cash transactions. Examples of general journal entries would be depreciation of fixed assets; correction of prior entries; increases to asset and debt accounts in the case of installment purchases of equipment; or similar transactions.

General Ledger

The *general ledger* is usually listed in account number sequence and divided into sections that correspond to the company's chart of accounts. The following number groups correspond to account categories in a typical system:

Balance Sheet Accounts

100s — Assets

200s — Liabilities

300s — Stockholder's or Owner's Equity

Income Statement Accounts

400s — Revenues

500s — Direct Costs

600s — Project Costs

700s — Administrative Expenses

800s — Other Income/Expenses

900s — Income Taxes

After the entire posting has been completed, it is a relatively simple matter to prepare financial statements from the general ledger. The 100, 200, and 300 account balances (plus net income) make up the balance sheet, and the 400 through 900 accounts make up the income statement. The general ledger also provides the starting point for the preparation of income tax returns.

ACCOUNTING BASIS AND METHODS

In the accounting system, *cash* and *accrual* are the two primary ways of recording income and expenses.

Cash Basis

The *cash basis* records income when money is received and records expenses when payment is made. The cash basis of accounting is the easiest form to maintain, but it fails to provide sound financial information. No attempt is made to match revenues with expenses and vice versa. In short, the cash basis will show what has been collected and paid out, but not necessarily what has been earned.

Accrual Basis

The *accrual basis* recognizes income when earned, even though it may not have been received, and records expenses when incurred, whether paid or not. This system attempts to match revenues and expenses for the period based on when events occur, not when funds change hands. The accrual form of accounting provides a better picture of actual performance than does the cash basis.

We can illustrate the different information that can be reported under the cash and accrual accounting methods with the same set of circumstances. Assume the following facts:

◊   Builders Construction Company completed a project in May.

◊   They received $50,000 in May and $30,000 in June.

◊   Materials for the job cost $45,000, with $15,000 paid for in May and the balance due in June.

◊   Labor costs for the project came to $22,000, with all but $2,000 included in payrolls prior to June 1st.

◊   Payroll overhead costs equaled 19% of payroll and were deposited by the due dates in June and July.

As shown in the example, on the following page, totally different numbers are obtained with the same facts. The accrual basis provides a much truer picture of the results of this particular project.

The income statement at May 31 would appear as follows, under the cash and accrual basis of accounting:

	Cash Basis	**Accrual Basis**
Revenues	$50,000	$80,000
Costs		
Materials	15,000	45,000
Labor	20,000	22,000
Payroll O/H	0	4,180
Costs of Construction	35,000	71,180
Gross Profit	**$15,000**	**$ 8,820**

FINANCIAL STATEMENTS

Through the bookkeeping process, information obtained from source documents such as checks, invoices, and receipts is entered into journals, summarized, and then transferred to the general ledger. The information in the general ledger is used to prepare financial statements that reflect the company's financial condition. Financial statements are prepared for both internal and external needs. Internally, the statements provide the following:

◊ the basis for short and long-term planning;

◊ an evaluation of completed and ongoing construction projects;

◊ information for future bids;

◊ necessary data to make equipment lease or purchase decisions; and

◊ information to prepare income tax returns.

Externally, financial statements provide information about the company for lending institutions, bonding companies, investors, and others with a close relationship to the contractor.

Financial statements consist of a *balance sheet, income statement,* and, though not as common, a *statement of cash flows.* The frequency of preparing financial statements varies with the need of the firm. At a minimum, statements are prepared annually. However, quarterly or monthly statements are much more common, even among smaller contractors, because of the drastic changes in financial condition that are possible in a short period.

The Balance Sheet

The balance sheet, or statement of financial position, as it is sometimes called, shows the financial condition of a company at a given point in time. It is a "snapshot" of the company—its assets, liabilities, and owner's equity—on a given date.

The balance sheet consists of two main parts. The first part shows the assets or items of value. The second part shows the liabilities (or debts) and the owner's equity. The total assets always equal the combined total of the liabilities and the owner's equity, thereby giving this financial statement its name—the balance sheet. This concept is reflected in the following formula:

$$Assets \quad = \quad Liabilities \quad + \quad Owner's\ Equity$$

To better illustrate the different accounting systems, the balance sheet (presented on page 8-9) is shown with both the cash and accrual basis of accounting. The accounts making up the balance sheet are grouped into different categories according to their particular characteristics, as described below.

Current Assets

In general, assets are items of value that the company owns. *Current assets* include cash and items expected to be converted into cash or to be consumed within the following year.

Other Assets

Other assets consist of such accounts as long-term investments, security deposits, prepaid expenses in excess of one year, and other items that do not qualify as either current or fixed assets.

Property and Equipment

Property and equipment are most commonly referred to as fixed assets. They consist of physical items acquired for use in the business, such as land, buildings, vehicles, equipment, tools, machinery, and furniture.

Current Liabilities

For the most part, liabilities consist of amounts due others and revenues that have been received, but not earned. *Current liabilities* are debts due within one year, including any long-term debt payment that is payable within the coming year.

Long-Term Liabilities

Long-term liabilities include debts exceeding one year, mortgages, unearned income, deferred income taxes, and similar long-term obligations. Income is unearned when money is received prior to performing the work. Deferred income taxes result from accounting differences between the tax return and the financial statements. For example, depreciation may be higher on the tax return, resulting in a smaller net income than shown on the financial statement. The deferred income taxes would compensate for this discrepancy by recognizing the tax liability on the difference in profit figures.

Stockholder's/ Owner's Equity

Stockholder's/owner's equity is the net worth of the company. It consists of the owner's investments and the accumulated earnings. If the company is a corporation (as in the sample balance sheet), equity accounts would commonly consist of the following:

◊ capital stock,

◊ additional paid in (over par value of stock),

◊ retained earnings (may also be broken down as appropriated or unappropriated), and

◊ current earnings (optional—may be included in retained earnings).

The equity section for sole proprietors will reflect an owner's capital account. This consists of the owner's investment and the accumulation of earnings and losses. A current earnings and owner's draw account may also be broken out in this section.

The Income Statement

The balance sheet reflects the financial condition of a firm at a point in time. The income statement (also called the profit and loss statement) shows the financial operations of the firm over a given *period* of time. Revenues are matched against costs and expenses to determine the net profit or loss for the period.

Different formats may be used for income statements depending on the informational needs of management. Additional details or explanations of income statement amounts are generally shown in schedules attached to the statement. The income statement on the following page shows a percentage breakdown of each element. By reviewing these percentages, management may quickly note how each element of the income statement relates to total revenues.

To better analyze the income statement data, the statement may include budgeted or planned income and expense amounts or prior year's figures for the same period. These added details assist comparisons with prior periods or planned performance.

The elements of the income statement include the following items.

Revenues

Revenues consist of the operating income from the normal business activity of the company. When the results of the business operation

BUILDERS' CONSTRUCTION CO., INC.
BALANCE SHEET
December 31, 20XX

	Accrual Basis	Cash Basis
Assets		
Current Assets		
Cash	$ 12,460	$ 12,460
Contract receivables	47,620	
Costs and estimated earnings in excess of billings on uncompleted contracts	12,475	
Employee advances	500	500
Inventories	1,240	1,240
Prepaid expenses	625	
Total current assets	74,920	14,200
Other Assets		
Deposits	5,000	5,000
Investment in joint venture	12,000	12,000
Total other assets	17,000	17,000
Property and Equipment, at cost		
Building	126,000	126,000
Equipment	16,500	16,500
Trucks and autos	22,460	22,460
Total Property & Equipment	164,960	164,960
Less: Accumulated depreciation	(28,750)	(28,750)
Net fixed assets	136,210	136,210
Total assets	$ 228,130	$ 167,410
Liabilities and Stockholder's Equity		
Current Liabilities		
Current portion, long term debt	$ 16,500	$ 16,500
Accounts payable	8,420	
Accrued payroll	2,340	
Accrued income taxes	5,620	
Billings in excess of costs and estimated earnings on uncompleted contracts	1,675	
Total current liabilities	34,555	16,500
Long Term debt		
Notes & mortgages payable	84,745	84,745
Deferred income taxes	1,280	
Total long term liabilities	86,025	84,745
Stockholder's Equity		
Common stock, $1 par value	10,000	10,000
Retained earnings	36,420	24,780
Current earnings	61,130	31,385
Total net worth	107,550	66,165
Total liabilities & equity	$ 228,130	$ 167,410

are reviewed, non-operating revenues are shown in a separate category (other income/expenses) to avoid confusion.

As previously discussed, the type of accounting method used will determine when income will be shown on the income statement. Revenues, along with costs and expenses, will vary under the cash and accrual bases and the different methods of accounting for long-term contracts.

Direct Costs

Direct costs are frequently referred to as prime or hard costs. They include those items that can be directly charged to specific projects. Materials, subcontracts, labor, equipment rentals, permits, bonds, and similar costs would be contained in this section.

Included in the labor cost is the labor burden or labor overhead, which consists of payroll taxes, insurance, and any other employee benefits.

Project Overhead

Project overhead (indirect costs) includes all construction costs that cannot be traced to a single project, but apply to a number of different jobs. While *direct costs* consist of variable costs (costs that increase in direct proportion to the volume of business), *indirect costs* include both fixed and variable costs. Fixed costs remain the same (within limits), even when the volume of work changes. For example, the salary of a superintendent will remain the same with minor differences in work volume; however, supplies will fluctuate directly with the volume of work. Vehicle expense is an example of a cost that contains both variable and fixed elements. Insurance and license fees will be the same, regardless of work, while fuel and maintenance costs will vary with the level of work.

General and Administrative Expenses

General and administrative expenses are costs that are apart from the actual construction projects, but are still associated with running a business. These expenses are common to all businesses and are frequently referred to as "company overhead". The sample income statement provides a typical listing of the general and administration (G & A) accounts that would be found in most companies.

Other Income/ Expenses

Other income/expenses are items not directly related to the company's primary business. For example, gains or losses resulting from the sale of assets are not directly related to a construction company's primary business.

BUILDERS CONSTRUCTION CO., INC.
INCOME STATEMENT
For the Year Ended December 31, 20XX
(Accrual Basis)

Revenues		
Construction Contract	$1,077,760	100.0%
Direct Costs		
Materials	420,640	39.0
Subcontractors	183,420	17.0
Labor	126,680	11.8
Other direct costs	16,310	1.5
Total direct costs	747,050	69.3
Project Overhead		
Superintendent salaries	72,290	6.7
Vehicle expense	8,470	.8
Supplies	6,220	.6
Depreciation – Vehicles	4,490	.4
Depreciation – Equipment	3,300	.3
Repairs	640	.1
Total Project Overhead	95,410	8.9
Costs of Construction	842,460	78.2
Gross Profit	235,300	21.8
General & Administrative Expenses		
Officer salaries	70,880	6.6
Clerical salaries	52,170	4.8
Professional fees	8,430	.8
Utilities	6,710	.6
Insurance	7,425	.7
Dues & subscriptions	840	.1
Office supplies	3,020	.3
Depreciation – office	6,630	.6
Licenses & fees	625	.1
Taxes	1,430	.1
Travel & entertainment	2,620	.2
Misc. expenses	480	0
Total G & A expenses	161,260	14.9
Income from Operations	74,040	6.9
Other Income/Expenses		
Gain on sale of asset	680	1
Interest income	75	
Interest expense	(9,485)	(.9)
Total other items	(8,730)	(.8)
Income before taxes	65,310	6.1
Provisions for income taxes	4,180	.4
Net income	$61,130	5.7%

Net Income

Net income (net profit) is the bottom line after all costs, expenses, and taxes have been deducted. In the case of sole proprietorships, partnerships and S corporations, taxes are not deducted in arriving at net income, but are instead reported on the owner's personal tax return.

The accounting process at work in the income statement can be summarized as follows:

$$Revenues - Costs\ of\ Construction = Gross\ Profit$$
and
$$Gross\ Profit - Expenses\ and\ Taxes = Net\ Income$$

Statement of Cash Flows

The statement of cash flows is a relatively new financial statement that has replaced the statement of changes in financial position. Where the balance sheet and income statement summarize general ledger accounts, the statement of cash flows examines the cash generation and distribution activities of the firm.

The information provided in this statement is designed primarily to help investors and creditors determine the company's ability to meet its obligations and produce positive cash flows. The statement of cash flows should provide useful information about how a company is using its cash from operations to repay debts, purchase equipment, expand capacities, and make other improvements. For example, the sample income statement for Builders Construction Company shows a net income of $61,130; however, the increase in cash was only $6,770. The various increases and decreases to the asset and liability accounts caused this difference between net income and the actual increases in cash.

The statement of cash flows presented is based on the sample balance sheet and income financial statements presented earlier in this chapter. The statement of cash flows classifies the cash flows according to their particular source (namely operating, investing, or financing activities). This grouping by source helps in analyzing the cash flow effects of the company's various activities, as well as providing useful information on trends and relationships within the groups. In short, this statement tells you where "it" (the money) came from and where "it" went.

Financial Statement Disclosures

Financial statement disclosures or notes provide information necessary to fully understand the company's financials. Financial statements are prepared from numerical measurement principles. The disclosures deal with factors that are qualitative in nature and are essential to the financials. The absence of disclosures could make the financial statements misleading by themselves.

BUILDERS CONSTRUCTION CO., INC.
STATEMENT OF CASH FLOWS
For the Year Ended December 31, 20XX
(Indirect Method)

Cash flows from operating activities:

Net income		$ 61,130

Adjustments to reconcile net income to net
cash provided by operating activities

Depreciation	$ 14,420	

Change in assets and liabilities:

Increase in contract receivables	(22,400)	
Decrease in inventory	480	
Increase in prepaid expenses	(65)	
Decrease in accounts payable	(2,480)	
Increase in accrued expenses	260	
Increase in deferred taxes	150	
Total adjustments		(9,635)
Net cash provided by operating activities		51,495

Cash flows from investing activities

Payment for investment in joint venture	(12,000)	
Capital expenditures	(31,600)	
Net cash used in investing activities		(43,600)

Cash flows from financing activities

Net borrowings under line of credit	500	
Principal payments under capital lease	(2,125)	
Proceeds from issuance of common stock	500	
Net cash provided by financing activities		(1,125)

Net increase in cash and cash equivalents		6,770
Cash and cash equivalents at beginning of year		5,690
Cash and cash equivalents at end of year		$ 12,460

The notes to a construction contractor's financial statements should include information concerning the accounting policies used by the firm to prepare the financials, events occurring after the date of the financials, pension plan obligations and funding, lease commitments, accounting changes, risks not reflected in the statements, details of long-term debt, and other matters needing explanation.

WORKING CAPITAL

Working capital is the difference between current assets and current liabilities. It is a measure of a firm's ability to meet its commitments for material purchases, payroll, debt repayments, and financial liabilities. The need for working capital in a construction firm is a result of timing differences between when obligations for materials and labor become due and when payment is received for the work. Frequently, the contractor must pay for materials, labor, and overhead to get a project started prior to receiving a progress payment from the owner or general contractor.

To further strain working capital, many contracts call for the owner or general contractor to retain a specific portion of the progress payment. This retention provides some form of assurance for the owner that the project will be properly completed. To aid a contractor in financing a project, it may be possible to obtain a line of credit for a specific contract.

Inadequate working capital (estimated by some experts to be anything less than a current ratio of 1.5 to 1) can result in cash flow problems, a financial inability to take on new work, and no cushion for a temporary slow period.

PAYMENT AND RETAINAGE

Payment practices in the construction industry are usually based on achieving the specific objectives that are spelled out in the contract. The way the payment is measured may be based on the completion of the component of the project, the reaching of a quantity measure (such as cubic yards of material installed), or at certain expenditure levels (for cost plus contracts). Frequently, the owner's representative (architect or engineer) will certify the stage of completion of quantities for progress payments.

Owners may include a provision in the contract for a certain part of progress payments to be retained. The amount held back may be:

◊ a fixed percentage of each payment until final completion;

◊ retention only until the project reaches a certain point (often 50%);

◊   no retention unless there are problems with progress or performance; or

◊   one of many other variations.

The amount retained by the owner from the general contractor is often in turn withheld from the subcontractor's progress payments. Additionally, the subcontractor's payments will likely be subject to a "contingent payment" provision in which payments will be made only after the general contractor has received a corresponding payment from the owner.

DEPRECIATION

With the exception of land, fixed assets are "written off" over a period of time or usage, based on their estimated useful life and any salvage value. This process of allocating the cost of the asset over time is called *depreciation*. Although there are a number of different ways of depreciating assets, the most common are the *straight-line* method and the *accelerated tax* method. Under the straight-line method, the cost minus any salvage value is written off uniformly over the life of the asset. The accelerated tax method ignores any salvage value and depreciates the asset according to a set formula over time periods, based on the type of property involved.

The following depreciation schedule of a backhoe purchased in July for $19,500, having a salvage value of $5,000 and a useful life of five years, illustrates these two depreciation methods.

ANNUAL DEPRECIATION		
	Straight Line Method	**Tax Method (Since 1987)**	**Percent Depreciated**
Year 1	$1,450	$3,900	20.0%
Year 2	2,900	6,240	32.0
Year 3	2,900	3,744	19.2
Year 4	2,900	2,246	11.5
Year 5	2,900	2,247	11.5
Year 6	1,450	1,123	5.8
Total Depreciation	14,500	19,500	100.0%
Salvage Value	5,000	N/A	
Total	$19,500	$19,500	

Often, one form of depreciation is used for tax purposes and another for presentation of financial statements.

FINANCIAL RATIO ANALYSIS

Financial ratio analysis is an important way of using and interpreting financial statements. A ratio is the relationship between two numbers on a financial statement. It is developed by dividing one number by the other. The resulting ratio provides information for examining company performance or trends. Comparing a company's financial ratios over time will help answer the questions, "Is performance better or worse?" and "What factors are contributing to the changes?" Ratios also make it possible to compare a company's performance with the average performance of businesses of similar age and size in the same industry. Creditors, bankers, investors, and sureties frequently use ratio analysis to make decisions on lending, financing, or bonding.

Financial ratios can be classified into the four basic types discussed below:

Liquidity ratios indicate the company's ability to pay its obligations in the coming year.

Debt/equity ratios, or leverage ratios, indicate the extent a company has been financed by debt, as opposed to owner's equity.

Activity ratios show the extent to which company assets are used, as well as the efficiency of the operation.

Profitability ratios measure the return on revenues and a company's investment in assets.

To illustrate the various types of financial ratios, examples of each type have been computed based on the accrual balance sheet and income statements that were presented earlier.

Liquidity Ratios

Current ratio is calculated by dividing the current assets by the current liabilities. A ratio of less than 1.0 would indicate an inability to pay for current liabilities as they become due or to finance new projects (lack of working capital).

$$\frac{\text{Current Assets}}{\text{Current Liabilities}} \quad \frac{74,920}{34,555} = 2.17$$

The 2.17 to 1 ratio reflects a good liquidity position for our sample company.

Quick ratio is a more severe test of liquidity. It requires deducting inventories from current assets before dividing by the current liabilities.

$$\frac{\text{Current Assets}}{\text{Current Liabilities}} \quad \frac{73,680}{34,555} = 2.13$$

Debt/Equity Ratios

Debt to equity ratios reflects the relationship of debt to owner's equity. This ratio provides an indication of the company's ability to obtain additional lending.

$$\frac{\text{Total Debt}}{\text{Equity}} \quad \frac{120,580}{107,550} = 1.12$$

The 1.12 to 1 ratio reflects that outside debt for the company slightly exceeds the owner's equity.

Activity Ratios

Average collection period ratio indicates the average number of days it takes to collect receivables. In construction, receivables can become difficult to collect. This ratio reflects the efficiency of the company in turning receivables into cash. Divide contract receivables by the daily average revenue (divide by 365 days) to determine this ratio.

$$\frac{\text{Current Receivables}}{\text{Revenue}/365} \quad \frac{47,620}{2,953} = 16.1$$

Profitability Ratios

Profit margin indicates the after tax profit on revenues. Net income is divided by revenues to determine the percentage profit on sales.

$$\frac{\text{Net Income}}{\text{Revenues}} \quad \frac{61,130}{1,077,760} = 5.7\%$$

Return on Investment

The *return on investment ratio* shows the profit earned on assets. This ratio indicates the efficiency to which assets have been used. A low return would suggest that the money invested in the business might be better placed elsewhere. Net income is divided by total assets to obtain the return on investment (ROI) percentage.

$$\frac{\text{Net Income}}{\text{Total Assets}} \quad \frac{61,130}{228,130} = 26.8\%$$

JOB COSTING

A job cost system allocates specific costs to a particular project. The primary value of this summary is to provide the contractor with:

◊ a method of evaluating current projects by showing the actual costs incurred, versus the original estimates; and

◊ a basis for bidding on future projects.

In short, job costing provides the contractor with the information necessary to maintain control over ongoing projects and insure an accurate base from which to estimate costs for future projects.

The job cost system identifies and tracks the direct costs (such as materials, subcontractors, and labor) associated with a given project. These costs are obtained from the following sources:

Labor	Time Sheets
Materials	Purchase Orders & Invoices
Subcontracts	Contracts & Invoices
Other Costs	Invoices

Additionally, project overhead costs are allocated to the project based on its share of total volume for the period.

The cost system tracks the various elements by specifically identifying them through a unique number code. A simple job cost numbering system might be developed in the following way.

◊ A project number could consist of consecutively numbered jobs preceded by the last digit of the current year. For example, the 16th project of 2005 might have the project number 516.

◊ The direct cost component number code would refer to the cost category of the disbursement, namely:

Labor	1
Materials	2
Subcontracts	3
Other direct costs	4

◊ A construction phase code could reflect the actual type of work being performed, such as concrete slab, plumbing, framing or electrical work. The system will become more complex as the construction work is broken further down into sub-phases. The construction of the concrete slab, for example, can be coded into more detailed phases such as excavating, forming, and pouring.

Using this system, a roofing material expenditure in the 16th project of 2005 could be coded in the job cost system as follows:

Project Number	Direct Cost Component	Construction Phase
516	2	21

Even a very basic job cost system, such as the one just described, can produce status and historical reports that are useful on both a daily scheduling basis and for future bidding. One such possible report would be the project phase analysis on the following page.

For a job cost system to be effective, it must be accurate and timely. Information is of limited value if it cannot be relied upon or is obtained too late to identify potential problems. Because of the detail required in job costing, computer based systems have proven much more cost effective than their manual counterparts.

Additionally, the computer can manipulate the data and produce a variety of reports from the same input in a fraction of the time that manual processing would take. This advanced technology makes this type of automation available to the smallest contracting firms. Use of computer technology should be seriously considered by all beginning contractors.

PROJECT 516 PHASE ANALYSIS

	Original Estimate	Cost to Date	Cost to Complete	Updated Estimate	Expected Variance
Concrete Slab					
516101 Labor	2,100	1,800	400	2,200	(100)
516201 Material	4,600	3,500	800	4,300	300
516401 Other	500	200	100	300	200
516501 Proj. O/H	300	200	100	300	0
Total	7,500	5,700	1,400	7,100	400
Plumbing					
516102 Labor	5,400	1,600	4,000	5,600	(200)
516202 Material	6,800	1,800	5,000	6,800	0
516302 Subs	600	700	100	800	(200)
516402 Other	100	0	100	100	0
516502 Proj. O/H	400	100	200	300	100
Total	13,300	4,200	9,400	13,600	(300)

CHAPTER 9
CONTRACT LAW

INTRODUCTION

Obviously, you have made a decision to enter into the construction business as a contractor. You should be aware at the outset that the construction business has many players other than the contractor. A construction job or construction project starts with a property owner who contracts with others to build and/or improve his or her property. Once the owner decides to construct a building or otherwise improve his or her property, the following players, and possibly others, become involved in the project.

Architect

The architect is usually the person who designs the building or other construction, draws up the plans and specifications for the project, and inspects the construction to assure that the plans are followed and the specified materials are used. Additionally, the architect will certify to the owner that a certain percentage of the work has been completed so that the contractor can receive progress payments.

Engineer

The engineer is usually a person who is skilled in some branch of engineering related to the construction project. A typical project may include a mechanical engineer, who is responsible for the air conditioning and related construction in the building. The project may also include an electrical engineer, who is responsible for the installation of the electrical system and related construction of the building. On some projects, the engineer is the designer of record working directly for the owner.

General Contractor

The general contractor, sometimes referred to as the "primary" or "prime" contractor, is the person who contracts directly with the owner and is responsible for the overall construction of the project.

Subcontractor

The subcontractor usually contracts with the general contractor to perform a specific portion of the construction project. A subcontractor may also contract with another subcontractor to perform a portion of the subcontract.

Craftsmen and Laborers

A craftsman is usually a person who is skilled in his or her trade, such as a bricklayer, cabinet maker, finish carpenter, tile setter, or other worker specializing in specific portions of the construction project. Laborers are usually the persons who are responsible for manual labor that does not require special construction skills.

Suppliers

On a typical construction project, all contractors involved will be required to supply the materials for their portion of construction. The company or person supplying the materials is referred to as the "material supplier."

WHAT IS A CONTRACT?

A contract is basically a legally binding agreement between two or more persons. A "person" may be an individual, corporation, partnership, limited liability company (LLC), or governmental agency. A contract should include all the terms and conditions of the agreement. When each person, or "party", agrees to all the terms, the contract is formed. At that point, each party is bound to do, or "perform", whatever duty, or "obligation", that the terms of the contract require of him or her. He or she must also perform his or her obligation in the way stated in the contract. If he or she fails to perform his or her obligation, or performs it in some other way, the other parties may sue him or her for breaking, or "breaching", the contract. For example, if John promises to build a deck for Al, and Al promises to pay John $100 a month for six months, then Al must pay John according to those terms. He cannot simply wait and pay all $600 at once. Similarly, if John promised to finish the deck in six weeks, he cannot wait and finish it in nine weeks. Contract breaches will be discussed more, later.

WHY DO I NEED A CONTRACT?

Contractors make contracts; that's what they do. The contractor agrees to build, remodel, reshape, repair, or otherwise do a job for the customer or owner. In return, the customer or owner agrees to pay the contractor money. This agreement is called a contract.

Since contractors almost always work through contracts, it is important for you to understand some basics about contracts. These basics are factors like what constitutes a contract, why contracts should be in writing, and the basic rules of forming and signing contracts. Understanding these principles can save a contractor a lot of time and trouble, not to mention money.

A properly drafted contract will assist the contractor in the event that a dispute arises with the owner, architect, subcontractors, or suppliers before, during, or after a construction project. This is especially true if the dispute goes to court. However, the most important reason for a thorough understanding of contracts and their proper use is to *prevent* disputes from arising in the first place. If all of the parties to an agreement completely understand what they must do, and what they can expect the other parties in the contract to do, then disputes should not arise.

MAKING A CONTRACT

You need three primary elements to make a contract. These are an offer, an acceptance, and consideration. Each of these elements will be discussed in detail below. Once these elements exist, the contract is formed and it is binding. For your protection, however, the offer and acceptance should be in writing. Although a verbal (or "oral") contract is binding under certain conditions, a written contract is easier to prove.

OFFER

Before any contract can be formed, one party must make an offer. It is important to understand the difference between an offer and negotiation. An offer must be clear and specific on the basic terms of the agreement, such as price, scope of work, and schedule. If any of these is not included, then it is merely a negotiation, not a true offer. The distinguishing factor between an offer and mere negotiation is that an offer clearly expresses an intent to enter into a certain contract if the other party agrees to the terms of that contract (i.e., accepts the offer). A common example of an offer is a bid. The bid sets forth an offer to do certain work under certain conditions for a certain price. If the bid is accepted, a contract is formed. An example of a statement, which would be mere negotiation rather than an offer, is "I can give you a great price for the electrical work on that building." If the party had said, "I agree to perform the electrical work in the building according to the specifications you have given me for the sum of $45,000.00," it would constitute an offer.

The significance of an offer, as opposed to negotiation, is that once an offer has been made, the party may become bound to the contract, based upon the actions of the other party (i.e., the acceptance of that offer). If the offer is left open for only a certain period of time, the other party must accept within that period of time in order to make a contract. If the offer is not explicitly left open for only a certain period of time, then it is deemed to be left open for a "reasonable time." Exactly what constitutes a "reasonable time" depends upon the facts and circumstances of the particular situation. If the offer is submitted in a certain manner, it is usually required that the offer be accepted in the same manner; for example, a written offer must be accepted in writing.

In order to avoid confusion, and to avoid entering into an ill-advised contract unintentionally, you should be very clear in your communications prior to entering into contracts. If you are making a formal offer to enter into a contract, but the price quoted by your suppliers could fluctuate, you should explicitly state that the offer will remain open only for a certain amount of time and make sure that the suppliers' contract will be good for that period of time. If you are attempting to negotiate a contract, but do not have enough information from the owner, architect, general contractor, your suppliers, or others, you should explicitly state that "this letter is for negotiation purposes, and does not constitute a formal offer." It is always better to be explicit and direct, regarding your intentions so that there will be no dispute later.

The offer, when accepted (as discussed below), may become the contract. Therefore, the offer should contain some essential elements, including the following items:

◊   the date of the offer and a specific time limitation for acceptance of the offer;

◊   the contractor's name, address, telephone numbers, person to contact, license number, and any other disclosures required by state law;

◊   the owner's name, addresses, and telephone numbers;

◊   the location of the construction site and a brief description of the work to be performed;

◊   reference to or identification of the drawings, specifications, and any other documents describing the work to be performed by the contractor;

◊   the total contract amount to be paid by the owner and the manner in which payment is required;

◊   the starting and completion dates of the work together with incidents such as "an act of God" that will automatically extend the completion date; and

◊   a clear and concise statement that you are offering to perform the work as shown on the documents for a specific sum. The offer may be a lump sum, cost of construction plus a percentage of the total cost for your fee, or a specific fee for your services, regardless of the cost of construction.

CONTRACT TYPES   The *lump sum* or *fixed price* contract is the most common type contract and requires the contractor to pay special attention to all costs and uncontrollable incidents that may affect the final cost of construction. The contractor agrees to complete the job for a stipulated sum and must bear the expense of any additional labor, material, and site improvement costs. He or she also has to bear the expense of other difficulties, such as labor disputes, inclement weather, theft, and other troubles not in his or her control. At the same time, the contractor gets to keep any cost savings that result from productive work or shrewd shopping. Of course, most owners prefer the lump sum contract, as it tells them exactly how much the job will cost. The contractor should avoid this type of contract unless the plans and specifications are such that the final cost can be easily determined in advance.

The *cost plus* contract is popular when the owner knows the contractor and is comfortable with the contractor's experience and workmanship. Usually, the owner and contractor will negotiate either a percentage of the actual cost of materials and labor for the contractor's markup or a fixed fee based upon the projected cost of labor and materials. The parties agree upon bonuses, based upon cost savings and early completion of the job.

The *unit price* contract is a form of the fixed price contract, but instead of giving the owner a lump sum price for the whole job, the contractor gives a price for each unit of work. For example, the contractor may agree to perform excavation for five dollars per cubic yard and place compacted fill for ten dollars per cubic yard. The final amount to be paid to the contractor is the sum of all the individual unit prices times the quantities of work done for each unit. This type of contract is usually reserved for projects where the exact quantities are not precisely known at the time of contract. Each unit price determined by the contractor in his or her bid contains enough money to cover his or her overhead and profit.

ACCEPTANCE

Once a true offer is made, the other party can accept it. The acceptance can be as simple as, "I accept your offer," but usually must be in the same form as the offer (as noted above). At that point, the contract is formed and both parties are bound. It is too late for either party to change his or her mind. It is important to note that the acceptance cannot change any of the terms of the offer. If it does, it is considered a counter-offer, which the other party may accept or reject. No contract is formed until both parties agree to all of the terms of the contract. This is commonly referred to as a "meeting of the minds." In other words, both parties agree to the same terms.

CONSIDERATION

Consideration simply means that each party must get something of value for the contract. For example, when John promises to build Al's deck, Al is receiving consideration. When Al promises to pay John, John is receiving consideration. This issue is much more likely to come up in other situations, such as donations, than it is in the context of a construction contract. However, it is possible for this issue to arise in the construction business. For example, if after Al and John have signed a contract for the deck, Al says, "If you do a good job and finish on time, I'll pay you an extra thousand dollars," this is not a contract. Al is receiving nothing in return for this promise. John was already obligated to do a good job on the deck and finish it on time. Therefore, John could not force Al to pay the one thousand dollars at the end of the contract because Al received no consideration for his promise to pay the extra one-thousand dollars.

ORAL VS. WRITTEN

Although oral contracts are normally binding, many types of contracts must be in writing, such as those transferring or encumbering real estate. In any case, oral contracts are never as good as a written document. The old saying, "An oral contract isn't worth the paper it's written on", is quite true. Most standard form contracts contain an "integration" clause that clearly states that the written contract supercedes any written or oral negotiations or agreements that are not contained in the written contract.

As mentioned above, a contract must include all the terms of an agreement. Without a written document spelling out all the terms and conditions of the agreement, if a misunderstanding or dispute arises over what the agreement was, it is extremely difficult to prove what those terms and conditions were. It is extremely important to have the terms, exactly as you understand them, put into a written document, and signed by all parties. Otherwise, you are at the mercy of the memory and honesty of the other party. This becomes even more important if the disagreement goes to court. In court, when a written agreement exists, the terms of that written agreement are the terms of the contract. The general rule (with limited exceptions) is that no oral agreements or modification can be used to contradict the written terms of the contract. Therefore, it is vital that you get all of the terms written down in the agreement. This especially includes things like how and when you are supposed to receive payment and the party responsible for obtaining permits, insuring the work site, and supplying the materials. The most common dispute arises when the owner presents a verbal "change order" and tells the contractor to change or depart from the written contract. These kinds of things may be understood or discussed, but it is still necessary to write them down.

It is obvious that no contract can cover every possible contingency that may arise. There is a presumption that every contract will be carried out in good faith by both parties according to the norm in the industry. For example, the contract may not specify that you are to use a certain type of material, but it is presumed that you will at least use material that is standard in the industry. Additionally, the contract may not specifically state how you are to be paid, but it is presumed that you will be paid in American money or by some valid, negotiable item, such as a check, but every item, which is left unsaid, leaves room for disagreement in the future. If the owner or customer wants only the highest-grade materials, this should be specifically stated in the contract, so that it can be accounted for in the price. If the contractor only wants to be paid by certified funds, delivered to his or her office, the contract should specifically provide as much.

OTHER ASPECTS OF CONTRACTS

There are two more things that you must have for a contract: a lawful object and capacity.

Lawful Object

The object of a contract is basically the reason the parties are making the agreement. For instance, the object of John and Al's contract is to have a deck built on Al's house. The law requires that all contracts have a lawful object. That means the purpose of the contract cannot be an illegal act. For instance, if the object of John and Al's contract is to build a swimming pool in Al's yard and a swimming pool is not allowed in Al's subdivision, the contract is voidable. If the object of the contract is not lawful, then the contract can be voided and is not binding.

Capacity

Capacity is just the ability to make binding contracts. To have capacity, a person must be mentally competent and have reached the age of majority. Basically, capacity requires only that the person be mentally and legally able to give a reasonable, rational consent to the agreement. Although the issue of the capacity of a party to enter into a contract will rarely occur in the contracting field, a related issue often arises: authority. Although a person may have the capacity to contract, he or she may not have the authority to enter into the contract in question. This is most likely to occur if you are contracting with an entity, such as a corporation, partnership, limited liability company, or governmental agency.

The person who signs on behalf of the entity must have the authority to represent that entity. If the entity is a corporation, the person who signs must have a corporate resolution authorizing him or her to sign the contract. The other entities have their own form of a resolution authorizing their representative to sign the contract. If there is any question about the person's authority to represent the entity, you should always confirm his or her authority by requiring a resolution that authorizes him or her to enter into the contract on behalf of the contracting entity. Remember, it is virtuous to trust, but wise to confirm. When in doubt, always require a resolution to confirm the person's authority to act for the entity.

CONTRACT INTERPRETATION

Interpreting a contract is generally an attempt to figure out exactly what the parties intended when they signed the contract. This usually occurs when a dispute arises between the parties. To standardize that process, several rules have developed in the interpretation of contracts.

If a provision in a contract is clear and the words have a plain meaning, that is the meaning that they will be given. This highlights the importance of clearly and specifically spelling out every term in the contract. When the provisions are clear and plain, and all parties act in good faith, there are rarely disputes between the parties over meaning. This rule usually comes into play in legal disputes when one party claims that the disputed provisions of the contract are "clear and explicit", while the other party claims that they are ambiguous. Therefore, you can see that this rule of interpretation of contracts is actually a statement of the obvious. The real question is whether or not the terms of the contract are actually clear and have a plain meaning.

In order to determine the plain meaning of words and phrases, it is sometimes necessary to check for special trade meanings or customary meanings. If a word has a special meaning in the construction trade, then that is the meaning it will probably be given in a construction contract. Sometimes it is also necessary to look at the context in which the word appears to determine its meaning.

If there is no plain meaning to a disputed provision by itself, then the contract must be looked at as a whole. When you consider the entire contract, the specific provision may have a clear meaning. Often provisions, which are confusing or ambiguous alone, make much more sense when you think about the general intent of the contract or the "big picture." These first two rules of interpreting contracts are basically common sense. Remember, the goal is to basically determine what the intent of each party was at the time when each party entered into the contract. Many provisions that seem confusing at first glance become very clear when one examines the entire context of the contract.

If the contract itself is vague on a specific point, you may find the true meaning based on the conduct of the parties. If both parties are acting as if the contract had a particular meaning on that point, then that is likely to be the interpretation given to that provision. For instance, assume John and Al's contract said only ". . . a deck beside the pool" but did not specify which side of the pool. If John has been building the deck on the north side of the pool for three weeks while Al watched, their conduct would indicate that they both intended the contract to mean the north side of the pool. Thus, if a dispute arose, the vague provision of the contract would probably be interpreted to mean the north side.

If nothing can be done to clarify the contract, then there is a general rule that the contract will be interpreted against the party who wrote it. This means that if you are providing the contract for the owner to sign, it is especially important to be very clear on the terms of the contract. If you use a standard contract form, as most contractors do, this rule will apply against you, and any ambiguity will be interpreted in favor of the owner.

BREACH OF CONTRACT

If any party fails to do anything required of him or her by the agreement, he or she has breached the agreement. There are two kinds of breaches—material and immaterial.

Material Breaches

A material breach of the contract is one that violates an essential aspect of the agreement: the owner refuses to pay, the contractor quits working on the project, or the contractor builds on the wrong site. These are the kinds of actions that qualify as material breaches. If one party commits a material breach, then the other party has some serious remedies available to him or her. First of all, he or she may refuse to perform his or her part of the agreement. You must be careful, however. If you refuse to fulfill your end because of a breach by the other party, you have to be sure it is a material breach. If it turns out to be an immaterial breach, then *you* are the one who has now committed a material breach. The non-breaching party may sue for monetary damages to pay for any loss he or she suffers as a result of the breach. This usually includes lost profits. In some cases, he or she may be able to sue to force the breaching party to perform his or her duty under the contract.

Immaterial Breaches

If a party fails to perform a less important duty, it may be considered an immaterial breach. For instance, a delay in the work, rather than a refusal to work, may be considered an immaterial breach, depending on the length of the delay and whether the time of completion was specifically made an important aspect of the contract. In the case of an immaterial breach, the non-breaching party may sue for monetary damages if he or she can show that the breaching party owed the duty and that he or she suffered a loss as a result of that party's breach of that duty. The non-breaching party cannot breach his or her duty by refusing to fulfill his or her end of the agreement. If he or she does, he or she is committing a material breach.

The issue of material versus immaterial breach can be a complicated and dangerous one. What may seem to be a material breach on the job may turn out to be considered immaterial, if it goes to court. It is very risky to try to determine for yourself that a breach is material, and then to react as if it is.

The bottom line is that either party is entitled to seek damages for any type of breach of the contract by the other party. Therefore, you should only refuse to perform your part of the contract if the other party has done something to prevent you from performing your part, or if the other party has breached a part of the contract, which goes to the very heart of the contract.

IMPORTANT CONTRACT TERMS

Agreement

The agreement is the document that the owner and the architect sign. It will spell out the name of the project and set forth the contract price. The project time will be specified in the agreement, as well as any liquidated damages. All other documents that are to be incorporated into the contract will be listed by reference.

Contract Documents

The term "contract documents" refers to all documents connected with the construction project, as stated in the general conditions. These documents include, but may not be limited to, the original request or invitation to bid, the contract between the owner and contractor, architect drawings and specifications, and any other document specifically related to the construction project.

Contractor's
Obligations

The contractor's obligations are clearly identified in the general conditions portion of the contract. These obligations include, but may not be limited to, the following duties:

◊ inspection of the construction site, along with a certification that the contractor is familiar with the site's condition;

◊ preparation and submission of material brands and/or samples, shop drawings, and installation methodology to the owner, architect, or engineer for approval;

◊ furnishing of a superintendent or other qualified person to supervise all aspects of the construction, including the supervision of subcontractors;

◊ arrangement for payment for all labor and materials used in the construction project (often, the owner is responsible for direct payment; however, the contractor is usually primarily responsible to the laborers and material suppliers);

◊ assurance that all required building permits, fees, and licenses are properly obtained and that all required inspections are made in a timely manner;

◊ selection and supervision of subcontractors and assurance that the building site remains clean and free from conditions that will create health hazards; and

◊ assurance that all construction commences when required by the contract, as well as maintaining of control to assure completion of the project as scheduled. In the event of delays caused by an act of God, or other incidents that provide for extensions to complete the job, obtain, in writing, the contract extension.

Owner's Obligations

Before and after signing the contract, the owner has various obligations. These obligations include, but may not be limited to the following duties:

◊ assurance that the construction project has met all zoning and code requirements prior to opening the bid process;

◊ interpretation of the contract and monitoring of the construction process as it progresses (the purpose of this obligation is to assure that construction is in compliance with the owner; the owner cannot ignore construction that is not in compliance and then complain later);

◊ review of the contractor's submission of materials, shop drawings, and construction methodology and approval or disapproval of these submissions—the final decision to accept or reject any substitutions rests with the owner; and

◊ assurance that all required payments to the contractor (and to others) are made in a timely fashion.

Drawings

This term refers to the plans prepared by the architect, draftsman, or engineer. The drawings should always specify the type of materials to be used and the quantity, size, and location of all components of the construction project. The contractor uses the drawings to prepare his bid and to solicit subcontractor bids. The architect is also responsible for supplying the exterior and interior designs for the project.

Specifications

The specifications supplement the drawings and are the detailed, precise descriptions of the components of the construction project.

Addenda

Addenda (plural for "addendum") are changes to the plans and specifications made after they are issued for bids, but before the bids are due. These changes become a part of the contract just as if they were in the documents at the time of issue.

Alternates

Some owners have an established budget for the work. Since they cannot know how much the bidders will offer to do the work for, they must be careful to issue plans that are likely to be within the budget. However, if the owner wants to get as much work as possible and still stay within the budget, he or she may use alternates. When alternates are specified, there will be a base contract for which a base bid will be given. Each alternate will describe some additional work or area of potential extra cost. The contractors will price each alternate so that the owner can have a menu of extra work from which to choose. Each state's laws vary, but usually on public work, the owner must accept the alternates in the order listed. This prevents the person who is in charge of spending the public's money from picking and choosing alternates, so as to favor one bidder over another.

Contract Price

This term refers to the total cost of the construction project, including all fees owed the contractor in a lump sum or fixed price contract. Contract price may also refer to the total cost of the construction project prior to paying fees to the general contractor in a cost-plus or fixed-fee contract. The term does not include fees paid to the architect or engineer, nor does it include other fees and charges that are not included in the contractor's obligation to pay.

Payment

This term refers to the manner, method, and frequency of payment to the contractor as the construction project progresses. It is imperative that the contractor confirms this item in the contract, as it affects his or her ability to make payment to suppliers and subcontractors.

Progress Payment

This term refers to the amount the contractor receives at the time when a specified portion of the job has been completed. Usually, the architect or engineer inspects the job and certifies that certain materials have been delivered and that a certain percentage of the job has been completed. The contract usually provides that the contractor file his or her other request for progress payments at a certain time prior to the date on which the progress payment is due.

Flow-Down Clauses

In most construction jobs, there are separate contracts between the contractor and the owner, and the contractor and the subcontractor. Most subcontracts include what are known as flow-down clauses. These clauses impose the same responsibilities and obligations upon the subcontractor that the prime contractor owes to the owner. This does not expand the scope of the subcontractor's work, however. It applies only to duties of the prime contractor related to the job of the subcontractor. For example, if the prime contract requires the prime contractor to give the owner ten days notice of work delays, then the subcontractor, according to the flow-down clause, must give the same ten days notice to the prime contractor. In this situation, it is important that the subcontractor read and understand the primary contract, even though he or she is not directly a party to it, because parts of that contract have been incorporated into his or her contract by reference. This could also occur in other contexts in which a contract incorporates another document into it by reference.

For example, it is quite common for a contract to refer to types of required insurance, governmental regulations, and separate plans or drawings. When a contract specifically incorporates other identifiable documents, these documents, in effect, become a part of the contract. Therefore, before signing a contract, you should make sure that you fully understand any separate documents which are incorporated into it.

Retainage

This term refers to a percentage of progress payments that is retained by the owner until the project is completed. The contract must specify that the owner is retaining a specified sum, and it usually states that the sum is payable to the contractor after the project is completed, provided that it is completed in accordance with the plans and specifications, and that the lien period has expired without the filing of liens on the project. The contractor should ensure that he or she has the right to withhold a retainage from his or her subcontractors and stipulate when the subcontractor is entitled to payment.

Time Extensions and Liquidated Damages

Almost all contracts have a specified contract completion date. In the event that no date is set forth in the contract, the courts will impose a "reasonable" time for the work. If the contractor does not finish by the contract completion date, he or she has breached his or her contract. For every day that the work is delayed, everybody—the owner, the contractor, and the designer—loses. Since the owners' damages for late completion are difficult to determine, they are often turned into money or liquidated. In other words, the contract will specify an amount to be paid, usually on a daily basis, if the contractor finishes late. If these damages are much higher than the owners' actual delay damages, many courts are hesitant to enforce them, since they no longer simply compensate the owner, but instead punish the contractor.

Most contractors will allow for the contract completion date to be extended for unforeseeable occurrences beyond the contractors' control. These clauses usually require that the contractor make his or her claim for an extension of the contract time with a specific number of days. (The AIA contract requires notice within 21 days.) A second requirement usually associated with claims for extra time is that the request be made in writing. If you feel that you deserve an extension of time, you should request it in writing regardless of whether you think you need it or not. The most common mistake that contractors make during the building of a project is to fail to make claims in writing in a timely manner. Many experts feel that this failure costs contractors hundreds of millions of dollars each year.

Final Payment

This term refers to the sum that is paid to the contractor after the completion of the project and after the lien period has expired. This payment not only includes the final progress payment, but also includes the entire retainage previously withheld by the owner.

Contract Changes

Although it is very common for changes to be made in a contract after the contract is signed, it is very important that these changes also be documented in some manner. If the owner requests a change (change order) in the construction which will cost additional money, you *may* be able to enforce that change in the contract and collect the extra payment if you prove that you have performed the additional work. However, you are much more certain to receive payment if this addition or change is done in the form of a written change order.

It is not necessary that a contract be written in any certain form. The standard AIA or other pre-printed standardized contracts are very useful, but not necessary. A contract in the form of a letter, signed by both parties, that sets forth all of the necessary terms and conditions, is just as enforceable. Similarly, it is not necessary that any changes in the contract be in any certain form. A simple letter stating, "I have agreed to perform _____ extra work, and you have agreed to pay _____ extra dollars", signed by both parties, may be sufficient. When in doubt, get it in writing.

One important rule to keep in mind is that you are presumed by law to know everything contained in a document which you sign. Neither party is entitled to claim at a later date that they did not know the contract stated a certain term or condition. Therefore, it is very important for you to thoroughly read and understand any contract before you sign it. If you do not understand a provision, or disagree with a provision, do *not* sign the contract until you understand the provisions fully and both parties agree to them. The time to change any of the provisions of the contract, including any of the preprinted provisions of a standard contract, is before you and the other party sign it. Standard contracts are prepared and supplied by various players in the construction industry and are designed to address some of the more difficult areas of contract involvement and interpretation. Although these contracts are designed to eliminate litigation, you should be aware that the forms are highly technical and should be carefully reviewed by you or a good attorney prior to signing them. Some of the more widely used and recognized standard forms are the American Institute of Architects Form (AIA), the Associated General Contractors Form (AGC), and the National Society of Professional Engineers Form (NSPE). Additionally, when bidding a public contract, the governmental agency or awarding authority will probably have developed a form for bidding and performing the construction project.

Warranty	This term refers to the owner's right to require the contractor to guarantee or warrant that the construction is in compliance with the plans and specifications. If there is defective work, the contractor must repair and correct the defect. If a material man or subcontractor furnished the work, the contractor can require that the responsible person repair and correct the defect.
Allowances	Many times, in lump sum contracts, there are some aspects of the work that are not completely defined at the time of contract. Examples include such items as light fixtures or brick. The cost of such items may be covered by an allowance. The contract will specify how much the contractor should "allow" for that portion of the work. The contractor figures this amount in his or her estimate and, therefore, his or her profit and overhead is figured on that cost. After the work commences, the owner will make his or her final choices, and the contractor will do the work according to those choices. If the cost of the work for which the allowance is given exceeds the allowance, a change order will be written increasing the contract amount. If the cost is less than the allowance, a change order for a credit will be prepared. The allowance amount typically includes sales tax, storage costs, and delivery charges.
Indemnification	This term is found in most contracts and is used to require the contractor (or another entity) to assume liability for injuries or other damages that occur on the owner's property, but are not the fault of the owner. This indemnity obligation is usually insured by the contractor through his or her general liability insurance policy.
Claims	A claim is an assertion by one party to the contract that he or she is entitled to extra money or extra time. Most contracts require that all claims be in writing and be made within a specified time. The specified time usually begins when the cause of the claim arises or when the claimant recognized that a claim exists. If the contractor does not make his or her claim in writing or on time, all is not lost. The reason for making timely claims is so that the other party can remedy the situation or mitigate the damages. Also, knowledge of the claim gives the other party the ability to gather information and otherwise document the condition. Many courts have decided that even though the contractor may not have abided by the exact requirement, if the owner is not prejudiced, that is his or her position is not harmed, the contractor may recover. For example, if the contractor can prove that the owner knew of the problem or extra work and acquiesced or went along with the whole thing, he or she can often recover.

Arbitration

Most standard form contracts contain an arbitration clause. If a problem occurs, either party may require that the dispute is settled by arbitration rather than by litigation.

Partnering

Partnering is a concept that is aimed toward reducing conflicts and claims on a project. In its most successful form, the owner and contractor hire a professional partnering firm to help them through the process. This facilitator usually meets with the major participants in a retreat format prior to the commencement of the work. At this partnering session, the facilitator will help the owner, contractor and contract administrator (usually the architect or engineer) to see that the parties share many goals in common. For example, all the parties want a job that finished on time and without claims. The facilitator will set up mock situations where several participants have to work together to solve common problems. After the job starts, it is much easier to keep a spirit of cooperation when problems arise, if the parties already know and trust one another.

CHAPTER 10
DOING BUSINESS IN
MARYLAND

The start up, operation, or expansion of a construction firm in Maryland generally involves the securing of one or more business, occupational, or environmental licenses. The number and type of licenses required will vary from company to company depending on the type of work involved, the company's form of organization, and other factors.

The state has provided the small business owner with a central point to obtain information and contacts for state regulatory requirements for operating a small business. This central point is called the Business License Information System (BLIS). The primary objective of this system is to help small business development in Maryland by offering a central location for determination of what licenses and permits must be obtained and maintained by individuals and businesses conducting their enterprise in the state.

BLIS also provides links from its web site, allowing the user to contact many state offices to order the forms necessary to obtain the required licenses, registrations, or permits.

The BLIS can be found at www.blis.state.md.us/client/blis.jsp.

CONTRACTOR LICENSING

To do business as a home improvement, electrical, plumbing, or heating, ventilation, air conditioning, and refrigeration contractor in Maryland, a contractor's license must first be obtained. The following chapter on licensing covers the home improvement licensing requirements in the state in more detail. Additionally, asbestos and lead abatement contractors must meet certain requirements before commencing work.

Contractor application forms and licensing information for the various types of contractor licenses in the state may be obtained from the following source:

Home Improvement Commission
(410) 230-6309
FAX (410) 333-0851
www.dllr.state.md.us/license/occprof/homeim.html

Board of Master Electricians
(410) 230-6270
FAX (410) 333-6314
www.dllr.state.md.us/license/occprof/elec.html

Board of Plumbers
(410) 230-6270
FAX (410) 333-6314
www.dllr.state.md.us/license/occprof/plumber.html

Board of Heating, Ventilation, Air
Conditioning and Refrigeration Contractors
(410) 230-6270
FAX (410) 333-6314
www.dllr.state.md.us/license/occprof/heat.html

All agencies are located at:

500 North Calvert Street
Baltimore, MD 21202-3651

Information regarding asbestos and lead-based paint requirements may be obtained from:

Maryland Department of Environment
1800 Washington Blvd.
Baltimore, MD 21230
(410) 537-3000
www.mde.state.md.us

STATE TAXES

The types of taxes a business must be concerned with will vary based on the type of business conducted, the form of the business structure, and whether there are employees. The Comptroller of Maryland is responsible for issuing tax licenses and numbers, as well as collecting the various taxes.

The comptroller has consolidated many of its registration services. It is now possible for new business owners to complete the necessary tax registration forms without unnecessary delays. The department has developed a Taxpayer Services Section to serve the diverse business community in the state.

Access to information on the services provided by the comptroller is available from:

Comptroller of Maryland
Revenue Administration Center
Taxpayer Services Section
110 Carroll Street
Annapolis, MD 21411

Business License (410) 260-6240
Central Registration (410) 767-1313
Corporate Income Tax (410) 260-7980
Employer Withholding (410) 767-1300
Sales & Use Tax (410) 767-1300
www.comp.state.md.us/

Chapter 13 contains more detailed information on sales, income, and payroll taxes.

FEDERAL TAXES

If your business is a corporation, partnership, or sole proprietorship with employees, it must be registered with the Internal Revenue Service for reporting and payment of income and payroll taxes. To obtain a federal Tax Identification Number, contact the Philadelphia office of the IRS at:

For instructions (215) 516-6999
Fax SS-4 Application Form to (215) 516-3990
or apply online at
www.irs.gov/businesses/

The Internal Revenue Service offers a variety of educational programs to assist business owners. Information on these programs can be obtained at the IRS Internet site under Small Business Workshop link. The site provides information on ordering Small Business Workshops on CD, an online classroom, and on-site locations and topics.

UNEMPLOYMENT

Businesses that have employees must register with the Maryland Department of Labor Licensing and Regulation for the reporting of payroll information and the payment of unemployment taxes. Registering information can be obtained from:

Department of Labor, Licensing & Regulation
Contributions Division
1100 North Eutaw Street
Baltimore, MD 21201
(410) 767-2414
www.dllr.state.md.us

Chapter 12 contains a detailed discussion on unemployment insurance in Maryland.

NEW HIRE REPORTING

New hire information, required by Federal law since 1997, must be reported, within 20 days, to the Maryland New Hire Registry.

The information required includes the employee's name, address, first day of work, social security number, and employee's availability of Medical benefits, salary, and pay frequency. Employer information includes name, address, federal EIN, and Maryland employment insurance number.

Reporting may be accomplished via:
◊ Electronic Reporting
  • Online at:
    https://newhirereporting.com/md-newhire/default.asp, or
  • By mail, using:
    ° 3.5 IBM Formatted Disk,
    ° CD-Rom IBM compatible, or
    ° 9-trackreel or 36 track cartridge.
◊ Non-Electronic Reporting – mail or fax:
  • Printed list,
  • New Hire Reporting Form, or
  • W-4 Form.

Mailing address:
  Maryland New Hire Registry
  P.O. Box 1316
  Baltimore, MD 21203-1316

Fax (410) 281-6004

Questions can be directed to the New Hire Registry at (410) 281-6000.

CORPORATIONS, LIMITED LIABILITY COMPANIES, AND LIMITED PARTNERSHIPS

To become a Maryland corporation, limited liability company, limited liability partnership, or limited partnership, formation documents must be filed with the Corporate Charter Division of the Department of Assessment and Taxation. Out-of-state entities (foreign) must be registered with the division before transacting business in the state or before obtaining any license or permit issued under Maryland law.

Information on the various filings may be obtained from:

Department of Assessments and Taxation
Corporate Charter Division
301 West Preston Street
Room 809
Baltimore, MD 21201
(410) 767-1340
www.dat.state.md.us

TRADE NAMES OR ASSUMED NAMES

Trade names or assumed names used by any business must also be registered with the Corporate Charter Division of the Department of Assessments and Taxation. This division can also reserve a business name for future use.

SAFETY

Maryland has adopted the federal OSHA standards for construction (part 1926), as well as adopting additional requirements that affect contractors. These additional requirements are summarized in Chapter 14.

The Division of Labor and Industry of the Department of Labor, Licensing and Regulation administers the Maryland Occupational Safety and Health (MOSH) Act. The MOSH Act covers every Maryland employer with one or more employees.

The department can be contacted at:

Maryland Occupational Safety and Health
1100 North Eutaw Street, Room 613
Baltimore, MD 21201
(410) 767-2215
www.dllr.state.md.us/labor/mosh.html

WORKERS' COMPENSATION

Maryland law requires all employers who employ one or more employees to provide workers' compensation coverage. This law provides financial protection for employees if they become injured or sick due to a job-related incident. A more detailed explanation of the law is contained in Chapter 12.

Further information concerning workers' compensation requirements can be obtained from:

Workers' Compensation Commission
10 East Baltimore Street
Baltimore, MD 21202
(410) 864-5100
FAX (410) 864-5101
www.wcc.state.md.us/

ENVIRONMENTAL

The Maryland Department of Environment is responsible for protecting the state's air, land, and water resources through the authority of state and federal environmental statutes. These laws regulate public and private facilities in the areas of air quality, water quality, hazardous waste, water supply, solid waste, mining, and underground storage tanks. The division issues and enforces all state permits in these areas, including asbestos contractor licensing, asbestos training provider approval, underground storage tank certifications, and lead paint accreditations. Contractors who work with lead *must* be accredited by the division.

Requests for specific information on environmental regulations and permit requirements and accreditations should be directed to:

Maryland Department of Environment
1800 Washington Blvd.
Baltimore, MD 21230
(410) 537-3000
(800) 633-6101
www.mde.state.md.us

CHAPTER 11
HOME IMPROVEMENT LICENSING
IN MARYLAND

IN GENERAL

The primary purpose of licensing is to protect the health and welfare of the public. Through the licensing process, applicants are screened to determine if they meet the minimum qualifications or standards, as set out by the legislature or licensing commission. Minimum requirements may include passing examinations, documenting work experience, providing evidence of financial solvency, and other information.

The licensing law includes penalties for anyone who operates as a contractor, subcontractor, or salesperson without a license. Additionally, the law gives the authority to the licensing commission to take disciplinary action against a licensee for violations of the law or regulations.

By establishing meaningful standards for licensing; setting requirements for the practice and conduct of licensed contractors, subcontractors, and salespersons; and keeping the unqualified, unethical, or dishonest from operating as contractors, subcontractors, or salespersons, the Maryland Home Improvement Commission protects the public.

The licensing law passed by the Maryland Legislature created the Maryland Home Improvement Commission and granted it the authority to adopt regulations necessary for the administration of this law. A complete text of the licensing law is located in Appendix A and the regulations are contained in Appendix B.

WHO NEEDS TO BE LICENSED?

Contractors, subcontractors, and salespersons engaged in home improvement require licensing in the state. Home improvement includes the following:

◊ the addition, remodeling, repair, or replacement of a building used as a residence, including structures or land improved adjacent to the building;

◊ driveways, fall-out shelters, fencing, garages, landscaping, porches, or swimming pools adjacent to a covered building;

◊ awnings, fire alarms, or storm windows in the building;

◊ work on individual condominium units; and

◊ connection, installation, or replacement of a dishwasher, disposal, or refrigerator with icemaker to existing plumbing lines.

Home improvement does not include the following:

◊ new home construction;

◊ work to comply with a new building guarantee of completion;

◊ appliance installation requiring alteration in the plumbing lines;

◊ sales of materials, if no installation is arranged or performed by the seller;

◊ work on apartment complexes of four or more single-family units;

◊ work on condominium common areas;

◊ shore erosion control projects;

◊ work by United States, state, or political subdivision agencies;

◊ work by employees of a contractor or subcontractor for wages (except salesperson);

◊ a telephone solicitor for a contractor;

◊ a licensed architect or electrical, plumbing, heating, ventilation, air conditioning or refrigeration contractor acting within the scope of their licenses; or

◊ a licensed security system technician.

With the exception of work to be done by the property owner, a permit for a home improvement must include the license number of a licensed contractor.

LICENSE ISSUANCE AND RENEWAL

Licenses are issued and renewed for a two-year period. Contractor fees are assessed for each place of business. License renewal applications received beyond two years of the expiration date will not be accepted for renewal and a new license application will be required. Renewal applications received after the expiration date will be effective on the date that the renewal requirements are fulfilled and will not be retroactive to the original expiration date.

A person may not reapply for a license within six months after being denied a license after a hearing or having the license revoked. As a condition for reinstatement of a suspended or revoked license, the person must pass an examination required by the Commission.

The Commission no longer issues temporary licenses.

LICENSE REQUIREMENTS

In addition to passing an examination designed to test the applicant's qualifications for the license type requested, applicants must submit an application form provided by the Commission.

Contractor applicants must also submit:

◊   proof of Worker's Compensation Insurance;

◊   evidence of $50,000 in general liability insurance coverage;

◊   documentation of two years of trade experience or comparable educational training;

◊   identification of corporate officers, partners, joint venture parties, and corporate or limited partnership resident agent, as appropriate;

◊   a current credit report; and

◊   proof of financial solvency (shown on Commission provided financial statement format).

Subcontractor applicants must also identify the principals associated with the business, as described for contractors, and submit a complete description of the nature of the business.

Salesperson applicants must describe their duties and provide a written notice affirming the employment or contractual relationship with a contractor. A salesperson may not represent more than two contractors at a time. When an individual ceases to be a salesperson for a contractor, the contractor must provide written notice of the disassociation to the Commission.

A licensee shall notify the Commission of a change in ownership, management, address, or trade name, within ten days.

INACTIVE STATUS

Licensees may apply to have their licenses placed on inactive status. Inactive contractors are not required to maintain liability insurance or pay guaranty fund assessments. Inactive licensees must continue to renew their licenses at reduced rates.

The license may be reactivated at any time by filing a $10 reactivation fee, submitting an application for reactivation, and meeting any requirements for licensure, such as liability insurance for contractors and the guaranty fund renewal assessment.

HOMEOWNERS GUARANTY FUND

A special fund has been established to reimburse homeowners who have suffered a loss that arose from an unworkmanlike, inadequate, or incomplete home improvement by a licensed contractor.

The fund is financed through an initial $100 assessment from contractors. Additional assessments may be required upon renewal. Currently, a renewal assessment of $100 is due with each two year renewal.

Recovery is limited to $15,000 to one claimant for a given contractor and a $100,000 maximum liability for all claims against a single contractor. Claims for attorney fees, consequential damages, court costs, interest, personal injury, or punitive damages are not covered by the fund.

DISCIPLINARY ACTIONS

The Commission may take disciplinary action by denying a license to an applicant, reprimanding a licensee, and suspending or revoking a license if the applicant, licensee, or management personnel:

◊ uses fraudulent or deceptive means to apply for or use a license;

◊ fails to provide required information regarding an application;

◊ fails to pass a required examination;

◊ is convicted of a felony or a misdemeanor that is directly related to home improvement;

◊ fails to perform contracts or deviates materially from plans and specifications;

◊ falsifies an account or fails to remit payments received to a contractor for a home improvement;

◊ engages in fraud;

◊ as a contractor or subcontractor:

- fails to show financial solvency, or

- lacks competence by performing unworkmanlike, inadequate, or incomplete home improvements;

◊ violates or attempts to violate the provisions of the home improvement law or regulations;

◊ engages in false, misleading or deceptive advertising;

◊ aides an unlicensed person to evade the licensing requirements;

◊ operates with a name other than that under which the license is issued; and

◊ advertises as a licensed entity without a license number in the advertisement.

CONTRACT REQUIREMENTS

Specific requirements are contained in the law regarding home improvement contracts. The requirements preclude a person from:

◊ making a substantial misrepresentation or false promise when obtaining a contract;

◊ committing fraud when executing or altering a contract, mortgage, promissory note or other document related to a home improvement;

◊ being involved in arranging a debt instrument that exceeds the price of the home improvement;

◊ demanding or receiving payment, before the contract is signed; or

◊ receiving a deposit of more than one-third of the contract price, upon execution of the contract.

Home improvement contracts should:

◊ be in writing and legible;

◊ describe each document that is a part of the contract; and

◊ be signed by each party.

Additionally, home improvement contracts shall contain:

◊ the name, address, and license number of the contractor;

◊ the name and license number of each salesperson who solicited or sold the home improvement;

◊ the date when work will start and be complete;

◊ a description of the work to be done and materials used;

◊ the price and, if financed, the number of payments, the amount of each payment, the finance charge, and a description of any security pledged; and

◊ a notice that provides the phone number of the Commission and states that each contractor and subcontractor must be licensed and that anyone may ask the Commission about a contractor and subcontractor.

If a contract contains a mandatory arbitration clause, the following information shall be included:

◊ the name of the person or organization that will conduct the arbitration;

◊ what fees will be charged;

◊ whether the findings are binding; and

◊ a disclosure that any claim against the Guarantee Fund will be stayed, pending the outcome of the arbitration proceeding.

The contracting parties shall place their initials and date adjacent to the clause at the time of execution of the contract.

PENALTIES

It is unlawful for any person, who is not currently licensed as a contractor, subcontractor, or salesperson, to engage in the business of home improvement. Individuals violating these provisions are guilty of a misdemeanor, punishable by a fine not exceeding $1,000 and/or by imprisonment not exceeding 30 days for the first conviction. Subsequent convictions may result in fines to $5,000 and imprisonment for up to two years.

Criminal violation of other provisions of the home improvement law results in misdemeanors, punishable by a fine of not more than $1,000 or imprisonment, not exceeding six months.

Civil penalties of up to $5,000 may be imposed by the Commission for each violation of the home improvement law.

DOOR-TO-DOOR SALES ACT

Sales characterized as "door-to-door" in the amount of $25 or more are subject to specific requirements and criminal penalties for willful violations. "Door-to-door" sales occur when the seller personally solicits the sale, including in response to an invitation by the buyer, and the sale is made at a place other than the seller's place of business.

A contract, subject to the Door-to-Door Sales Act, may be cancelled without penalty or obligation within three business days from the date of the transaction, by mailing or delivering a signed and dated copy of the Notice of Cancellation to the seller.

"Door-to-door" sales do not include sales:

◊ made after prior negotiation at the seller's place of business;

◊ subject to being rescinded under the federal Consumer Credit Protection Act;

◊ initiated by the buyer to meet an emergency and the buyer provides a statement describing the emergency and waiving the right to cancel;

◊ made entirely by mail or telephone;

◊ initiated by the buyer for maintenance or repair of personal property (does not exclude additional services or goods); and

◊ of real property, insurance, or securities by a registered broker.

Unlawful Practices

Under the Door-to-Door Sales Act, it is regarded as an unfair or deceptive trade practice for a seller to:

◊ fail to furnish the buyer with a fully completed receipt or contract, a statement as to cancellation rights, and a "Notice of Cancellation" properly filled out;

◊ include any waiver of the buyer's right to cancel in a contract;

◊ fail to orally advise the buyer of cancellation rights at the time of purchase;

◊ misrepresent the buyer's right to cancel;

◊ fail to honor a valid cancellation and refund all payments, return any trade-in, cancel any obligation of the buyer, or notify the buyer of the disposition of any seller's goods within ten days;

◊ convey any indebtedness of the buyer to a third party before the end of the fifth business day after the transaction date;

◊ fail to immediately identify the solicitor, including providing proper identification, the trade name of the person represented, and the kind of goods or services offered; and

◊ misrepresent the seller's true status or mission.

The buyer may cancel unfair or deceptive sales by any means of notification to the seller.

Penalties

Sellers violating the provisions of the Door-to-Door Sales Act are subject to civil judgments for damages and attorney fees, as well as injunctive actions and criminal sanctions. Violations are regarded as misdemeanors, subject to a fine of not more than $1,000 or imprisonment for not more than one year.

A text of the Door-to-Door Sales Act is contained in Appendix C.

CHAPTER 12
STATE LABOR LAWS

In addition to the federal laws governing employee-related issues covered in the general section of this publication (see Chapter 7, Employer Obligations), the State of Maryland imposes several requirements on employers.

Some state regulations, such as workers' compensation and unemployment insurance, are totally separate from the federal law, while others (minor labor for example) complement the federal requirements.

WORKERS'
COMPENSATION

Maryland employers are required to comply with Maryland's Workers' Compensation Law. The law provides a remedy for workers who are injured or suffer an occupational disease "as a result of and in the course of employment." It provides a comprehensive benefit structure for injured employees. The law defines the method for determining compensation to an injured employee based on wages and the extent of the injury. It provides wage loss benefits, as well as reimbursement for medical expenses related to the compensable injury. It also requires reasonable and necessary vocational rehabilitation training.

The state Workers' Compensation Commission administers the provisions of the Law and acts as an adjudicator where a dispute arises between the parties as to workers' rights or employers' obligations.

The law requires every firm, corporation, or private person with one or more employees, full or part-time, to provide workers' compensation coverage. Employers obtain coverage through one of three ways:

◊ Contracting with private insurance companies licensed to write workers' compensation insurance in Maryland,

◊ Qualifying as self-insurers by receiving approval from the Workers' Compensation Commission, or

◊ Participating in the Injured Workers' Insurance Fund.

Employers' duties to employees and to the Commission include:

◊ Posting a Workers' Compensation Poster in a prominent place used by employees, and

◊ Reporting accidents that result in a disability to an employee of more than 3 days on a First Report of Injury Form, within 10 days with the Workers' Compensation Commission. Copies are also sent to the employer's insurance carrier and to the Division of Labor and Industry. (Filing a First Report Injury Form does not mean that an employee claim has been filed.)

Employers who refuse or neglect to obtain workers' compensation insurance shall be guilty of a misdemeanor, fined up to $5,000, imprisoned for up to one year, or both fine and imprisonment.

UNEMPLOYMENT INSURANCE

The Maryland Department of Labor, Licensing, and Regulation administers the Maryland Unemployment Insurance Law.

A "new" employer opens an unemployment insurance account by filing a <u>Combined Registration Form</u> no later than 20 days after the first day of business. This single application covers reporting requirements for seven state agencies.

The application can also be filed on the Internet at www.marylandtaxes.com. Help is also available on **The Employers' Line** at 1-800-492-5524.

An "employer" is defined as an individual or employing unit which employs one or more individuals for some portion of a day. "Employment" is defined as any service performed for payment whether full-time or part-time. This includes salaries paid to corporate officers.

Employers are assigned one of the following tax rates:

◊ New Account Rate—for a "new employer" that does not qualify for an experience (earned) rate. The rate for new employers is the average of the rate for all employers in the state for the last five years.

◊ Standard Rate—for an employer who is eligible for earned rate but failed to file quarterly tax and wage reports; or

◊ Experience (Earned) Rate—for employers who paid employee wages in two fiscal years. The employer is assigned a tax rate reflecting the employer's own experience. Employers transferring all or part of their business from another state to Maryland may be eligible to transfer their experience rate to Maryland.

Only employers pay unemployment taxes. The tax may not be deducted from employees' wages.

Employers are required to file quarterly wage and tax returns on the Contribution Return (DLLR/OUI 15) and on the Employment Report (DLLR/OUI 16). Employers with more than 100 employees are required to submit quarterly wage information on magnetic tape. Employers with fewer employees are also encouraged to use "diskette reporting" as their method for submitting quarterly wage information.

For unemployment purposes, the annual taxable wage base limit in Maryland is $8,500 before deductions. Returns and payment are due by the end of the month following the end of the calendar quarter.

It is the employer's responsibility to post two unemployment benefits eligibility posters (DLLR PUB/OUI 6116 Health Insurance Coverage and DLLR/OUI 328 Employees Rights Under Maryland's Unemployment Insurance Law) in locations readily accessible to employees.

EMPLOYING MINORS

The State of Maryland Department of Labor, Licensing and Regulation, Division of Labor and Industry administers and enforces the Wage Payment and Collection Law and oversees the issuance of work permits for minors. The Maryland Employment of Minor's Law compliments the federal Fair Labor Standards Act. Minors, ages 14 through 17, may only work with a work permit. This permit must be in the employer's possession before the minor is permitted to work. Minors, under the age of 14, are prohibited from employment. In addition, no minor, under the age of 16, can be employed on a construction site.

MARYLAND WAGE LAWS

In addition to enforcing several labor laws, the Employment Standards Service of the Maryland Division of Labor and Industry publishes The Maryland Guide to Wage Payment and Employment Standards booklet. The following summary information is from the booklet. The booklet is available free of charge by downloading from the Department of Labor, Licensing and Regulation web site at www.dllr.state.md.us, by contacting the office of Employment Standards Service at the number listed, or by sending an e-mail to ess@dllr.state.md.us.

Division of Labor and Industry
Employment Standards Service
1100 North Eutaw Street, Room 607
Baltimore, Maryland 21201
(410) 767-2357
FAX (410) 333-7303

**Wage Laws
in General**

The Maryland's Wage Payment and Collection Law governs which employees receive wages, how often employees must be paid, guidelines for wage deduction, prohibited actions, and how employees may enforce their rights.

The Wage and Hour Law governs minimum wage and overtime and applies to employers who do not meet the coverage requirements of the Federal Fair Labor Standards Act. The Law also provides minimum wage standards that vary from the Federal Fair Labor Standards Act. The primary difference is that the age of a minor or the immigration status of an alien has no bearing on a worker's rights to receive earned wages.

Note: The following summary of the various wage laws do not include all exceptions.

**Remedies for
Unpaid Wages**

The law provides three remedies for employees to collect unpaid wages:

◊   Filling a claim with the Employment Standards Service,

◊   Filing a lawsuit, or

◊   Filing a criminal charge.

Work Issues

Work issues are defined in the law as including:

◊   Defining "work" as service performed by an employee at the request and under the control of an employer for which an employee is entitled to be paid;

◊ Providing the right to change work hours, shifts, or times for employment at the employer's discretion; and

◊ Making the distinction between an employee and an independent contractor.

Wages and Compensation

Wages and compensation include the following:

◊ Defining "wages" as payment and compensation for work performed including bonuses, commissions, fringe benefits, or any other "remuneration" promised for work performed.

◊ Frequency of pay must be at least every two weeks or twice a month.

◊ Paying employees their final wages at termination on or before the day the employee would have been paid if the employment had not terminated.

◊ Setting a schedule for regular paydays to pay all earned wages on time. If a scheduled payday lands on a holiday weekend or other non-workday, pay is due the day before.

◊ Taking deductions from wages is prohibited unless:

- The court has ordered or allowed the employer to make the deduction;

- The Commissioner of the Maryland Division of Labor and Industry has allowed the deduction to offset or "pay for" something of value the employee has received, such as personal loans or wage advances;

- Allowed by some law or regulation of the government, such as federal and state taxes; or

- The employee has given express written authorization for the deduction, such as repayment to the employer for a loan.

◊ An employer may not make any deduction for unemployment and workers' compensation premiums.

◊ Unused vacation time at termination is payable, unless the employee was informed at the time of hiring that unused vacation leave will be forfeited when employment ends.

◊ Unused sick leave at termination is generally not payable, unless expressly allowed in a contract or in an employer's policy.

◊ The law does not guarantee days off for holidays or special holiday pay for private sector employees.

◊ Employers are not required to pay wages during temporary closures, such as snow emergencies.

◊ An employer, in the absence of a contract, may lower an employee's wage rate at any time with one full pay period advance notice.

◊ Severance pay is not guaranteed unless promised in advance in an employment contract, agreement, or policy.

◊ The cost of providing and maintaining a uniform may be passed on to the employee—with the employee's signed written authorization.

◊ An employee must be paid for all time that the employer requires an employee to be at work, including driving time from the employer's place of business to the work site and back to the place of business.

◊ Employers are not required to pay wages for the time it takes an employee to commute to work.

◊ When an employee provides notice of termination to the employer, the employer is not required to allow the employee to work the period provided in the termination notice.

◊ Employees must be paid for training time and meetings when attendance is required or expected by the employer.

◊ Employees must voluntarily authorize employers to direct deposit wages.

◊ Employers are responsible for keeping employee records consisting of the employee's name, address, occupation, rate of pay, amount paid each pay period, and the number of hours each day and each work week for a period of three years in or about the place of employment.

◊ An employer may not keep any part of an employee's wage, by withholding an entire paycheck, part of a paycheck, or incremental wage deductions from several paychecks as security against some future or contingent occurrence.

◊ Paying wages with a bad check is the same as failing to pay wages and carries the same civil and criminal penalties.

◊ Employers are not required to provide breaks for rest or lunch for workers over 18. If breaks over 20 minutes are provided, wages are not paid if employees are allowed to leave the workplace and they are not expected "to be on hand" to work.

◊ Commissioned sales agreements between employee and employer are generally enforceable contracts.

Overtime

Overtime, generally, is payment to an employee of one and one-half times the regular hourly wage for work performed in excess of 40 (actually worked) hours in a 7-day week. Those exempt from the provisions include:

◊ Executive, administrative, and professional employees,

◊ Outside salespersons,

◊ Commissioned employees (subject to a minimum wage requirement),

◊ An employer's immediate family members, and

◊ Independent contractors.

As noted above, independent contractors are exempt from the overtime requirements. Additionally, all wage and employment laws do not apply if a true independent contractor relationship exists. A signed independent contractor agreement is not, by itself, enough to establish the relationship. The economic reality of the relationship determines the worker's status.

The following basic principles may apply in determining whether a worker is an employer or an independent contractor:

◊ Who has the right to control and direct the work being done, not only as to the result to be accomplished, but also to the details and means by which that result is accomplished?

◊ Who has the right to discharge a worker?

◊ Who furnishes tools, material, etc.?

In general, independent contractors are persons who are in business for themselves, offering their services to the public.

Employer Discretion in the Workplace

Employer discretion in the workplace provisions includes:

◊ Employees work "at the will" of their employers. They can generally be hired or fired for almost any reason, except one that discriminates on the bases of race, color, gender, national origin, religion, age, disability, or marital status;

◊ The Maryland Economic Stabilization Act calls for voluntary employer guidelines regarding employees as to advance notification of reductions in operations, provision on information on continuation of benefits, and mechanisms for state assistance. Employers must notify their local Office of Unemployment Insurance when laying off 25 or more employees for a common reason for periods in excess of 7 days;

◊ Employers can set the terms of employment unless there is an employment contract with stated limitations. An employer may require an employee to work on holidays, to work at night, or to perform extra or different duties than the employee was originally hired to perform, as the need may arise for the employer. An employer may also treat one employee differently than other employees, such as by providing compensation at a different rate of pay. As in the case of employment termination, however, the power to do these things is limited by the prohibition against illegal discrimination/retaliation.

◊ Employers are not required to provide benefits such as vacation, sick leave, holidays and holiday pay, health and life insurance, bonuses, and severance pay; and

◊ Employers, at their own expense, following specific legal procedures for a legitimate business purpose, may require employees to be tested for the illegal use of alcohol and drugs.

CHAPTER 13
BUSINESS TAXES AND
REPORTING REQUIREMENTS

Contractors in Maryland are subject to a variety of taxes and reporting requirements at the state level, in addition to those required at the federal level. The nature and intent of these taxes and reports varies depending on the structure of the business, the size of the payroll, residency status, and location of the business.

The on-line Combined Registration Application (CRA) is a quick and easy way to register a business and apply for the various business tax accounts, such as the employer withholding account and the sales and use tax license. The form is available at www.marylandtaxes.com.

This section summarizes the most frequently encountered taxes and reports required of contractors doing business in Maryland.

STATE INCOME TAX

Domestic and foreign corporations, and corporate members of partnerships are subject to an annual state income tax and must file an annual return even if no taxes are due. Corporations file on Form 500 and pay taxes, if due, at the time of filing.

S Corporations, partnerships, and Limited Liability Companies are not required to file on Form 500, but are required to file as pass through entities on Form 510. These filings are information returns and a tax payment is not due with the return since taxable items are passed through and taxed at the individual, partner, or shareholder level.

The corporate rate is a flat 7% of the corporation's federal taxable income after state modifications. State income taxes are filed on Form 500 and are due on the 15th of the month following the end of the tax year or period. A copy of the federal tax return for the same period must be attached to the Maryland tax return.

There are more than a dozen business tax credits for which businesses may be eligible, including some for the creation of new jobs or the development of businesses in Enterprise Zones. Credits are claimed on Maryland Form 500CR.

**SALES AND
USE TAX**

The State of Maryland Sales and Use tax is calculated at 5% of the sale, lease, or use of materials obtained in or brought into the state. There is no general local sales tax in the State of Maryland. A Sales and Use Tax License is required and may be obtained when filing the Combined Registration Application noted above.

When materials or supplies are purchased for use in the operation of a business from a Maryland vendor, the purchaser is regarded as the consumer of all materials used in the process and pays the sales tax on the items at the time of purchase.

If materials and supplies are purchased from an out-of-state vendor who does not collect Maryland sales tax, the purchaser must pay the sales (use) tax on those items to the state. If the out-of-state seller collects another state's sales tax equal to, or greater than, the Maryland tax, then no tax is due. If the tax collected is less than the Maryland tax, then the difference in sales tax is due.

Sales and Use Taxes are due and payable monthly on the 21st of the month following the previous month. The Comptroller of the Treasury will provide the required forms. Filing must be done on the form provided and not a photocopy of the form.

**STATE TAX
WITHHOLDING**

Employers in Maryland must withhold Maryland State Income Tax from all resident and non-resident employees, with few exceptions. The amount of tax to withhold is based on the information provided by employees on the Employee's Exemption Certificate (Form MW507), as applied to the Maryland withholding charts. Employees who do not provide an Exemption Certificate have taxes withheld on the basis of no exemptions.

Employers may withhold based on the "withholding tables" or the "percentage method tables" both of which have been updated as of January 1, 2004.

Taxable wages include all compensation to an employee for services performed. For the purpose of the withholding tax, taxable wages include salaries, commissions, bonuses, fees, or any other item of value paid to an individual for services performed as an employee.

Employers are required to obtain a withholding account number by registering with the Maryland Comptroller of the Treasury. The

Combined Registration Application, noted earlier in this chapter, will help to facilitate the process.

Withholding taxes are reported and remitted on Form MW506, on a monthly, quarterly, annual, or seasonal basis.

◊ Monthly reports and payments are required when the withholding is more than $700 a quarter. The report and payment is due by the 15th of the following month for the preceding month.

◊ Quarterly reports and payments are required when the withholding is less than $700 a quarter. Quarterly reports are filed on the 30th of the month following the preceding quarter.

◊ Annual reports are required when the withholding is less than $250 a year. The reports are due on January 31 for the previous year.

◊ Seasonal reports for employers who only operate during certain months of the year are available for those employers who obtain prior approval to file seasonally.

Employers must file a zero report if no taxes are due. The report is filed using the Maryland TeleFile Service at (410) 260-7225.

Effective January 1, 2004 a new accelerated filing category was created. Employers who withheld $15,000 or more in the preceding tax year and who have accumulated $700 or more in current withholding must file their returns within three business days of the payday.

BUSINESS LICENSING TAX

The Maryland Home Builders Registration Act requires any person or business that builds or sells new homes in Maryland to be registered with Office of the Attorney General, Consumer Protection Unit.

Any person or business organization must obtain a construction license from the appropriate Clerk of the Circuit Court on an annual basis if the person or organization agrees:

◊ to do work on or in any building or structure, requiring the use of paint, stone, brick, mortar, wood, cement, structural iron or steel, sheet iron, galvanized iron, metallic piping, tin, lead, electric wiring or other metal, or any other building material;

◊ to do any paving or curbing on sidewalks or streets (public or private property); or

◊ to excavate earth, rock or other material for foundations or any other purpose.

Licenses are issued by the Clerk of the Circuit Court and are renewed annually (May 1st). Licensing fees are $30 for Cecil County, $40 for Baltimore City, $15 in all other counties and $50 for all out of state companies.

A Home Improvement License is required if you perform any home improvement work in Maryland. Home improvement work includes alteration, remodeling, repair, or replacement of any building used as a residence, including individual units of a condominium complex. Contractors who hold a license under the Maryland Home Improvement Law are not required to obtain a construction license issued by the Clerk of the Court.

See Chapter 11 for more information on the licensing and regulation of contractors, subcontractors, and salespersons by the Commission.

BUSINESS PERSONAL PROPERTY TAX

In Maryland there is a tax on business owned personal property. The tax is imposed and collected by the local governments and administered by the Maryland Department of Assessments and Taxation.

Personal property includes furniture, fixtures, office equipment, machinery, tools, supplies, inventory, and other property not classified as real estate. For tax purposes, personal property is valued annually.

All corporations, limited liability companies (LLC), limited liability partnerships (LLP), limited partnerships (LP) and business trusts must file a personal property tax return whether or not they own property. Sole proprietorships and general partnerships must file a return only if they possess business personal property or need a business license.

The annual tax return must be filed by April 15th of each year with a valuation of business personal property, located in Maryland, as of January 1 of the prior year.

If you are unsure whether you are required to file, contact the Maryland Department of Assessments and Taxation at (410) 767-1170 if you are operating as a Corporation, LLC, LLP, LP or Business Trust. If you are a sole proprietorship or general partnership, the contact number is (410) 767-4991.

The Department of Assessments and Taxation can also be reached on the Web at http://www.dat.state.md.us.

CHAPTER 14
MARYLAND SUPPLEMENTAL
SAFETY INFORMATION

The William-Steiger Occupational Safety and Health Act of 1970 (OSHA) provides that states may elect to assume the responsibility for development and enforcement of a state occupational safety and health program.

In 1971, the Governor designated the Division of Labor and Industry as the agency responsible for Maryland's Occupational Safety and Health Plan (MOSH). Authority and enforcement responsibility was assumed in 1973 and, in 1985, the Maryland program received final approval and full enforcement authority in all subject areas covered by the state plan.

The MOSH Act covers every Maryland employer in a business, trade, commercial, or industrial activity, who has one or more employees, including state and local governments. The Act does not affect workplaces covered under certain other laws such as the Atomic Energy Act, the Federal Mine Safety and Health Act, and the Longshoremen's and Harbor Workers' Compensation Act. The MOSH Act also does not apply to working conditions of employees of the federal government or any agency or instrumentality of a federal government agency. Those workers are covered under the Federal OSHA program.

SAFETY AND HEALTH PROGRAM

The MOSH agency suggests that all occupational safety and health programs include five elements to be an effective occupational safety and health program. The level of detail and complexity with which a program will address these five elements will vary from employer to employer. However, all programs will include, at some level, each of the following five elements:

◊   management commitment and employee involvement,

◊   work-site inspection and analysis,

◊   hazard prevention and control,

◊   safety and health training, and

◊   long-term commitment of the employer.

The following steps are recommended for developing an effective safety program:

◊ Develop a plan of action that includes management and employee involvement.

◊ Designate a person to be responsible for safety and health.

◊ Determine the safety and health requirements for the particular workplace and operations.

◊ Conduct a hazard assessment of the workplace and provide for regular safety and health inspections.

◊ Correct identified hazards and develop a method of tracking the correction of hazards.

◊ Train employees in safety and health.

◊ Keep the program up-to-date and effect.

◊ Develop knowledge of the safety and health requirements of the company's particular trade.

◊ Develop a general safety and health policy, safety rules, and other operational procedures.

◊ Train a core of supervisory employees in MOSH and OSHA Standards.

◊ Conduct individual site preparation (pre-job survey).

◊ For on-site operations:

  ▪ post emergency telephone numbers,

  ▪ mark exit routes; and

  ▪ ensure the availability of emergency equipment before work begins.

Each safety and health program must be specific to the site and the operations of the company, taking into consideration the size of the organization, the workplace operations and exposures, the personnel capabilities, and available resources.

MOSH does **not** consider these approaches satisfactory:

◊ written handouts with no opportunity for discussion, and

◊ audio-visual presentations with no opportunity for discussion.

Employee training is a long-term commitment. Training will need to be repeated periodically. Retraining should be scheduled on an annual basis, except when employee actions indicate a need for earlier or more frequent retraining.

New employees need training prior to starting work that would expose them to hazards. Transferred employees will also require training whenever they are exposed to new hazards. This need is reflected by the disproportionately high injury rates among workers newly assigned to work tasks. Although some of these injuries may be attributable to other causes, a substantial number are directly related to inadequate knowledge of job hazards and safe work practices.

DOCUMENTATION

An important part of a safety and health program is adequate documentation. Proper documentation should provide:

◊ a historical reference that can be reviewed to determine program effectiveness;

◊ an accessible document to which management and employees can refer when unsure of proper procedures; and

◊ evidence of the employer's efforts to provide a safe and healthful work environment.

It must also be remembered that many of the standards require some form of documentation for sampling results, medical surveillance, equipment inspection, personal protective equipment programs, and other activities.

All employers are required to have the following:

◊ the MOSH poster (posted);

◊ OSHA Forms 300, 301, and 300A (see Chapter 6);

◊ a written Hazard Communication Program;

◊ administrative control programs, where used in lieu of engineering controls; and

◊ emergency procedures.

Employers may also be required to maintain information on the following, if required by applicable standards:

◊ Environmental monitoring, including noise and chemical sampling.

◊ Exposure control programs required under many of the air contaminant standards.

◊ Employee medical records, as part of any medical surveillance program.

◊ Records of employee testing for personal protective equipment programs, when respirators or hearing protection is required.

◊ Certifications for inspection programs for cranes and forklifts.

At a minimum, it is also recommended that the employer maintain some level of documentation for the following:

◊ any employee training,

◊ safety rules and procedures for employees,

◊ workplace self-inspections,

◊ equipment maintenance programs, and

◊ accident investigations.

The conditions that make safety and health programs so important in the construction industry can also make these programs difficult to effectively administer. These conditions include:

◊ Dispersed and frequently changing work environments.

◊ The simultaneous use of work sites by several contractors.

◊ Frequent turnover in personnel.

◊ The need for specialized training and equipment in hazardous operations.

MOSH is available as a resource in obtaining information and acquiring answers to compliance questions. MOSH provides a free consultation program to assist small businesses with on-site problems.

The MOSH Training and Education section also provides several publications, of interest to contractors, available online at www.dllr.state.md.us/labor/pub.html. These publications include the following helpful items:

◊ Developing a Workplace Safety and Health Program.

◊ Access to Information about Hazardous and Toxic Substances.

◊ MOSH Construction Checklist for Self-Inspection.

TRAINING OF POWER EQUIPMENT OPERATORS

Each employer who hires employees to operate power equipment is required to develop and carry out an employee safety-training program designed to inform and train employees in the safe operation of power equipment.

Power equipment includes: backhoes, bulldozers, front-end loaders, skid steer equipment, gradalls, scraper pans, cranes, and hoists.

Each employer must keep, on file, records of the training given, a written description of its employee training program, and where the training was given.

HIGH VOLTAGE ACT

Maryland High Voltage Line Act applies to electric lines that are installed above ground level and have a voltage of more than 750 volts. Unless determined otherwise, any line above ground is presumed to be energized and over 750 volts.

The provisions of the act apply, if it is anticipated that any part of an object or person will come within ten feet of a high voltage line while performing an activity. The code also covers exemptions, notifications, warning signs, and right of inspection.

STAIRWAYS, LADDERS, AND SCAFFOLDS

The OSHA standards apply to all stairways, ladders, and scaffolds used in construction, alteration, repair (including painting and decorating), and demolition of work sites. The standards also specify when stairways, ladders, and scaffolds must be provided.

Ladders

Ladders shall be capable of supporting the following loads without failure:

◊ A self-supporting portable ladder – at least four times the maximum intended load;

◊ An extra-heavy-duty type 1A metal or plastic ladder – at least 3.3 times the maximum intended load; and

◊ A portable ladder that is not self-supporting – at least four times the maximum intended load.

When portable ladders are used for access to an upper landing surface, the ladder side rails shall extend at least three feet above the upper landing surface or, when such an extension is not possible because of the ladder's length, the ladder shall be secured at its top to a rigid support that will not deflect, and a grasping device, such as a grabrail, provided.

Non-self-supporting ladders shall be placed so that the horizontal distance from the top support to the foot of the ladder is approximately one-quarter of the working length of the ladder (the distance along the ladder between the foot and the top support).

Scaffolds

Each scaffold and scaffold component shall be capable of supporting its own weight and at least four times the maximum intended load.

Each end of a platform, 10 feet or less in length, may not extend over its support more than 12 inches, and a platform greater than 10 feet in length may not extend over its support more than 18 inches, unless the platform is designed and installed so that the cantilevered portion of the platform is able to support the load without tipping, or has guardrails which block employee access to the cantilevered end.

Guardrail systems shall be installed along all open sides and ends of platforms. Guardrail systems shall be installed before employees, other than erection crews, release the scaffold for use. The top edge height of toprails or equivalent member on supported scaffolds shall be installed between 39 inches and 45 inches above the platform surface.

Each toprail or equivalent member of a guardrail system shall be capable of withstanding, without failure, a force applied in any downward or horizontal direction at any point along its top edge of at least 100 pounds for guardrail systems installed on single-point or two-point adjustable suspension scaffolds, and at least 200 pounds for guardrail systems installed on all other scaffolds.

PROTECTIVE EQUIPMENT

Personal protective equipment should not be used as a substitute for proper engineering, work practice, or administrative controls. Personal protective equipment should be used in conjunction with these controls to provide for employee safety and health in the workplace. Personal protective equipment includes all clothing and other work accessories designed to create a barrier against workplace hazards. The basic element of any management program for personal protective equipment should be an in-depth evaluation of the equipment needed to protect against the hazards at the workplace. Management dedicated to the safety and health of the employees should use that evaluation to set a standard operating procedure for personnel, and then train employees on the protective limitations of personal protective equipment and on its proper use and maintenance.

Using personal protective equipment requires hazard awareness and training on the part of the user. Employees must be aware that the equipment does not eliminate the hazard. If the equipment fails, exposure will occur. To reduce the possibility of failure, equipment must be properly fitted and maintained in a clean and serviceable condition.

Selection of the proper personal protective equipment for a job is important. Employers and employees must understand the equipment's purpose and its limitations. The equipment must not be altered or removed even though an employee may find it uncomfortable. (Sometimes equipment may be uncomfortable simply because it does not fit properly.)

ACCESS TO INFORMATION ABOUT HAZARDOUS AND TOXIC SUBSTANCES

Maryland has enacted legislation requiring that employees be given information about hazardous substances in the workplace. The law requires employers to obtain, maintain, and submit certain information. It applies to employers of one or more employees and covers more than 50,000 chemicals, as well as hundreds of thousands of products.

The following steps, provided by the state, assist employers in achieving compliance with the law and providing safe and healthy working conditions for employees.

◊   Make an inventory of all material that may be hazardous.

◊   Obtain Material Safety Data Sheets (MSDS) (see Chapter 6).

◊ Use the information on the MSDS to determine the chemical name and to identify the hazards of the substance.

◊ Prepare a chemical information list.

◊ Send the chemical information list to the Maryland Department of the Environment.

◊ Develop a system for updating the list.

◊ Conduct a hazard assessment.

◊ Check to see that all containers are labeled.

◊ Develop an employee training and notification program.

◊ Train and educate employees.

◊ Document the training given.

◊ Develop a written hazard communication program.

PERSONAL MEDICAL INFORMATION

Under Maryland law, the release of personally identifiable employee medical information is limited to protect the substantial privacy interests involved in employee medical records. To ensure that no information is released without proper safeguards, the law requires that medical information be:

◊ retained only for the amount of time needed;

◊ kept secure while being used; and

◊ not disclosed, except in narrowly defined circumstances and as permitted or required by law.

EXCAVATION STANDARDS

OSHA defines an excavation as any man-made cut, cavity, or depression in the earth's surface formed by earth removal. This can include excavations for anything from basements to highways.

The excavation standards apply to underground tunnels, shafts, chambers and passageways. They apply to cut-and-cover excavations, both physically connected to ongoing construction tunnels and those that create conditions characteristic of underground construction. These hazards include reduced natural ventilation and light, difficult and limited access and egress, exposure to air contaminants, fire and explosion.

The Maryland excavation safety guidelines require that:

◊ Every excavation, five feet or greater in depth, must be protected from cave-in. Excavations of less than five feet must also have a protective system or design, if inspection reveals a cave-in hazard.

◊ Inspections conducted by competent persons must be:

- daily, prior to the beginning of work;

- as needed, through the work day; and,

- after any hazard increasing occurrence (i.e., rainstorms, changes in temperature, vibrations and superimposed loads).

Inspections must include, at a minimum, the review of:

◊ Surface encumbrances,

◊ Underground installations,

◊ Access and egress,

◊ Exposure to vehicular traffic,

◊ Falling loads,

◊ Mobile equipment warning systems,

◊ Water accumulation,

◊ Adjacent structure,

◊ Stability,

◊ Loose rock or soil,

◊ Fall protection, and

◊ Hazardous atmospheres.

FALL PROTECTION

In the construction industry in the U.S., falls are the leading cause of worker fatalities. Each year between 150 and 200 workers are killed and more than 100,000 are injured as a result of falls at construction sites. OSHA recognizes that accidents involving falls are generally complex events, frequently involving a variety of factors. Consequently, the standard for fall protection deals with both the human and equipment-related issues in protecting workers from fall hazards. For example, employers and employees need to do the following:

◊ Where protection is required, select fall protection systems appropriate for a given situation.

◊ Use proper construction and installation of safety systems.

◊ Supervise employees properly.

◊ Use safe work procedures.

◊ Train workers in the proper selection, use, and maintenance of fall protection systems.

OSHA has revised its construction industry safety standard and developed systems and procedures designed to prevent employees from falling off, onto, or through working levels and to protect employees from being struck by falling objects.

The standard identifies areas or activities where fall protection is needed. These include ramps, runways and other walkways, excavations, hoist areas, holes, formwork and reinforcing steel, leading edge work, unprotected sides and edges, overhand bricklaying and related work, roofing work, precast concrete erection, wall openings, and other walking/working surfaces. The standard sets a uniform threshold height of 6 feet (1.8 meters), thereby providing consistent protection. This means that construction employers must protect their employees from fall hazards, whenever an affected employee is 6 feet or more above a lower level. Protection also must be provided for construction workers who are exposed to the hazard of falling into dangerous equipment.

Under the standard, employers are able to select fall protection measures compatible with the type of work being performed. Fall protection generally can be provided through the use of guardrail systems, safety net systems, personal fall arrest systems, positioning device systems, and warning line systems.

FIELD SANITATION   OSHA Standards require that potable water, toilets, food handling operations, and other employee field facilities conform to sound hygienic principles.

A potable water supply shall be provided in all places of employment and consist of:

◊   containers capable of being tightly closed and equipped with a tap (no dipping);

◊   clearly marked containers, not used for any other purpose; and

◊   a sanitary container for unused cups and a receptacle for disposing of used cups (common drinking cup prohibited).

CHAPTER 15
LIEN LAWS

State law provides for the filing of liens against real property to secure payment to those supplying labor or materials on a project. The lien law does not apply to federal or state public works.

LIEN DEFINED

A lien is a right to secure payment for work or materials furnished to improve real property (land or buildings). A properly filed lien results in an unpaid obligation recorded against the title to the property, similar to a mortgage on a building. If the obligation is not satisfied, the sale of the property may be forced to satisfy the lien.

WHO MAY LIEN?

To be able to file a lien to secure an amount due, a contract with the owner is not necessary. Those who supply labor, materials, or furnish rental equipment at the site of construction or improvement without a contract with the owner may also file. In addition to new construction, those repaired, rebuilt, or improved to 15% of their value are subject to liens.

To perfect or properly complete a lien may require several very specific steps filed with various entities in a very exact time frame. Courts generally require strict compliance with the provisions of the lien law and will dismiss improperly filed liens.

The following is an overview of the key elements of the lien law. It is not meant to be a complete description of the steps necessary to perfect a lien. Legal advice should be obtained for specific help in protecting and asserting lien rights.

FILING CLAIMS

Those entitled to file a lien against real property must file proceedings in the circuit court in the county where the project is located. The lien must be filed within 180 days after the work has been finished or materials furnished.

The petition to establish the lien must contain at least the following information:

   ◊   the name and address of the person claiming the lien;

   ◊   the name and address of the owner of the property;

◊ a description of the property upon which the lien is claimed;

◊ a statement of the amount due, with all credits given;

◊ a statement as to what, when and for whom the work or materials were done or furnished; and

◊ evidence that the required notice was properly served or posted, if the claimant is a subcontractor.

The right to enforce a lien expires one year from the day on which the petition to establish the lien was first filed. During the year period, the claimant may file a petition to enforce the lien or execute on any bond given to release the lien from the building or land.

A building or land may not be subjected to a lien if, prior to the establishment of a lien, legal title has been granted to a bona fide purchaser for value.

EXTENT OF LIEN

Properly established liens shall apply to the following:

◊ The land covered by the building and as much other adjacent land belonging to the building's owner as may be necessary for the ordinary purposes of the building. Designation of land boundaries may be established and recorded with the circuit court prior to construction.

◊ The extent of work done or materials furnished if a building is commenced and not finished.

◊ Only to the extent of the tenant's interest in the construction or repair, remodeling or improvement of at least 25% of a building's value.

NOTICE TO OWNER

Anyone contracting with another, other than the owner, to do work or furnish material is not entitled to a lien unless, within 120 days after doing the work or furnishing the materials, they provide written notice of an intention to claim a lien.

Additionally, a notice given to cover work or materials for a single family dwelling being erected for the owner's personal residence on the owner's land applies only to the amount the owner is indebted under the contract at the time of the notice.

The Notice of Intention to Claim a Lien shall contain the following information:

◊   the name of the person filing the Notice;

◊   the description or designation of the property;

◊   a brief description of what, when, and for whom the work was done or materials furnished; and

◊   the amount earned to date and the amount unpaid.

The notice is effective if given by registered or certified mail, return receipt requested, or personally delivered to an owner. If notice cannot be given on account of absence of the owner or other cause, the claimant may place the notice on the door or other front part of the building before a competent witness within the required time.

A construction contract between a contractor and another to supply work or materials may not contain language that requires the waiver of the right to claim a lien or sue on a contractor's bond. Likewise, contracts that condition payment from the contractor on the receipt of payment from the owner may not waive the right to lien or sue.

Upon settlement or payment in full by the owner, the contractor shall provide a release of lien form each material supplier and subcontractor who provided work or materials under the contract.

The complete text of the Lien Law is located in Appendix D.

APPENDIX A

MARYLAND HOME IMPROVEMENT COMMISSION
CODE OF MARYLAND
BUSINESS REGULATION ARTICLE
TITLE 8. HOME IMPROVEMENT

Subtitle 1. Definitions; General Provisions

§ 8-101. Definitions.

(a) In this title the following words have the meanings indicated.

(b) "Commission" means the Maryland Home Improvement Commission.

(c) "Contractor" means a person, other than an employee of an owner, who performs or offers or agrees to perform a home improvement for an owner.

(d) "Contractor license" means a license issued by the Commission to act as a contractor.

(e) "Fund" means the Home Improvement Guaranty Fund.

(f) "Hearing board" means a home improvement hearing board appointed by the Commission under § 8-313 of this title.

(g) (1) "Home improvement" means:

(i) the addition to or alteration, conversion, improvement, modernization, remodeling, repair, or replacement of a building or part of a building that is used or designed to be used as a residence or dwelling place or a structure adjacent to that building; or

(ii) an improvement to land adjacent to the building.

(2) "Home improvement" includes:

(i) construction, improvement, or replacement, on land adjacent to the building, of a driveway, fall-out shelter, fence, garage, landscaping, porch, or swimming pool;

(ii) connection, installation, or replacement, in the building or structure, of a dishwasher, disposal, or refrigerator with an icemaker to existing exposed household plumbing lines;

(iii) installation, in the building or structure, of an awning, fire alarm, or storm window; and

(iv) work done on individual condominium units.

(3) "Home improvement" does not include:

(i) construction of a new home;

(ii) work done to comply with a guarantee of completion for a new building project;

(iii) connection, installation, or replacement of an appliance to existing exposed plumbing lines that requires alteration of the plumbing lines;

(iv) sale of materials, if the seller does not arrange to perform or does not perform directly or indirectly any work in connection with the installation or application of the materials;

(v) work done on apartment buildings that contain four or more single-family units;

(vi) work done on the commonly owned areas of condominiums; or

(vii) a shore erosion control project, as defined in § 8-1001 of the Natural Resources Article, for a residential property.

(h) "Home improvement contract" means an oral or written agreement between a contractor and owner for the contractor to perform a home improvement.

(i) (1) "License" means, except where it refers to a license other than one issued under this title, a license issued by the Commission.

(2) "License" includes:

(i) a contractor license;

(ii) a subcontractor license; and

(iii) a salesperson license.

(j) "Licensed contractor" means a person who is licensed by the Commission to act as a contractor.

(k) "Owner" includes a homeowner, tenant, or other person who buys, contracts for, orders, or is entitled to a home improvement.

(l) "Salesperson" means a person who sells a home improvement.

(m) "Salesperson license" means a license issued by the Commission to sell a home improvement.

(n) "Sell a home improvement" means:

(1) to negotiate or offer to negotiate a home improvement contract with an owner; or

(2) to seek to get a home improvement contract from an owner.

(o) "Subcontractor" means a person, other than a laborer or supplier of materials, who makes an oral or written agreement with:

(1) a contractor to perform all or part of a home improvement contract; or

(2) another subcontractor to perform all or part of a subcontract to a home improvement contract.

(p) "Subcontractor license" means a license issued by the Commission to act as a subcontractor.

§ 8-102. Scope of Title.

(a) This title does not apply to a transaction of:

(1) the United States or an instrumentality of the United States; or

(2) a state or an instrumentality or political subdivision of a state.

(b) A county or municipal corporation of the State may not:

(1) require a person to get authorization to do business performing or selling a home improvement; or

(2) regulate the qualifications necessary to do that business.

(c) This title does not limit the power of a county or municipal corporation:

(1) to regulate the character, performance, or quality of a home improvement by having a system of inspections and permits designed to:

(i) ensure compliance with and help to enforce applicable State and local building laws; or

(ii) enforce other laws necessary to protect the public health and safety; or

(2) to adopt a system of inspections and permits that requires:

(i) submission to and approval by the county or municipal corporation of plans and specifications for an installation, before construction of the installation begins; and

(ii) inspection of work done.

§ 8-103. Waiver Prohibited.

The provisions of this title may not be waived.

Subtitle 2. Established

§ 8-201. Established.

There is a Maryland Home Improvement Commission in the Department.

§ 8-202. Membership.

(a) (1) The Commission consists of 7 members, appointed by the Governor with the advice of the Secretary.

(2) Of the 7 members of the Commission:

(i) 3 shall have experience in some phase of the business of home improvement;

(ii) at least 1 shall have experience in the business of banking or finance; and

(iii) 3 shall be consumer members.

(b) Each member of the Commission shall have been a citizen and resident of the State for at least 5 years before appointment.

(c) Each consumer member of the Commission:

(1) shall be a member of the general public;

(2) may not be a licensee or otherwise be subject to regulation by the Commission;

(3) may not be required to meet the qualifications for the professional members of the Commission; and

(4) may not, within 1 year before appointment, have had a financial interest in or have received compensation from a person regulated by the Commission.

(d) While a member of the Commission, a consumer member may not:

(1) have a financial interest in or receive compensation from a person regulated by the Commission; or

(2) grade any examination given by or for the Commission.

(e) Before taking office, each appointee to the Commission shall take the oath required by Article I, § 9 of the Maryland Constitution.

(f) (1) The term of a member is 4 years and begins on July 1.

(2) The terms of members are staggered as required by the terms in effect for members of the Commission on October 1, 1992.

(3) At the end of a term, a member continues to serve until a successor is appointed and qualifies.

(4) A member who is appointed after a term has begun serves only for the rest of the term and until a successor is appointed and qualifies.

(g) The Governor may remove a member for incompetence or misconduct.

§ 8-203. Chairman.

With the advice of the Secretary, the Governor shall designate a chairman from among the members of the Commission.

§ 8-204. Quorum; Voting; Meetings; Compensation; Office.

(a) (1) A majority of the authorized membership of the Commission is a quorum.

(2) The Commission may not act unless at least a majority of the authorized membership concur.

(b) (1) The Commission shall meet at least once a month.

(2) The Commission may hold meetings at the times and places in the State that it determines.

(c) Each member of the Commission is entitled to:

(1) compensation in accordance with the State budget; and

(2) reimbursement for expenses under the Standard State Travel Regulations, as provided in the State budget.

(d) The Commission shall have its office in Baltimore City.

§ 8-205. Executive Director.

(a) (1) The Secretary shall appoint an executive director of the Commission.

(2) The executive director serves at the pleasure of the Secretary.

(b) The executive director shall devote full time to the duties of office.

(c) The executive director is entitled to:

(1) compensation in accordance with the State budget; and

(2) reimbursement for expenses under the Standard State Travel Regulations, as provided in the State budget.

(d) While employed as executive director, the executive director shall be covered by a surety bond in the form and amount required by law.

(e) The executive director shall:

(1) administer and operate the office of the Commission;

(2) be responsible to the Secretary;

    (3) keep the official records of the Commission; and

    (4) keep the seal of the Commission.

§ 8-206. Staff.

    (a) (1) The executive director may employ a staff in accordance with the State budget.

    (2) Except as otherwise provided by law, the staff is in the skilled service or professional service, with the exception of special appointments, in the State Personnel Management System.

    (b) The executive director shall employ an investigative staff in accordance with the State budget.

    (c) The executive director may contract with an expert, subject to the State budget, if the services of an expert are required in a particular case.

    (d) Investigative staff and contractual experts shall investigate only complaints about home improvement.

§ 8-207. Regulations.

    (a) The Commission may adopt and enforce regulations to carry out this title.

    (b) (1) The executive director shall:

        (i) compile and keep in the office of the Commission a set of current regulations adopted under this title; and

        (ii) make a copy of the regulations for anyone who asks for one.

    (2) The Commission may set a fee to cover the cost of making and mailing a copy of the current regulations.

§ 8-208. Administration and Enforcement by Commission.

    (a) The Commission shall administer and enforce this title.

    (b) (1) If the Commission concludes that continuing conduct of a person alleged to be in violation of this title will result in irreparable or substantial harm to any other person, the Commission may sue for:

        (i) injunctive relief against the conduct;

        (ii) an order for satisfactory completion of a home improvement contract; or

        (iii) restitution.

    (2) If the Commission sues for injunctive relief under this subsection against a person who is not licensed under this title, the Commission need not:

        (i) post bond; or

        (ii) show that no adequate remedy at law exists.

    (3) A suit under this section shall be brought in the circuit court for the county where:

        (i) the alleged violation occurs; or

        (ii) the principal place of business of the alleged violator is located.

§ 8-209. Records.

(a) The Commission shall keep available for public inspection during office hours a record of:

    (1) all licenses issued under this title;

    (2) all expirations, revocations, and suspensions of those licenses; and

    (3) all contractors represented by each salesperson who holds a license under this title.

(b) The Commission shall collect a fee of $1 per page for each copy of a document in the Commission office.

§ 8-210. Certification of Licensing Status.

The Commission shall collect a fee of $1 for certifying under seal the licensing status of a person.

§ 8-211. Contractor List Supplied to Counties.

Each month the Commission shall give the building and permits department and the office of consumer affairs of each county a current list of all licensees and may provide other information relevant to this title.

§ 8-212. Miscellaneous Powers and Duties.

(a) The Commission at any time may require of an applicant or licensee:

    (1) information reasonably related to the administration or enforcement of this title; and

    (2) the production of financial records.

(b) The Commission shall have a seal.

§ 8-213. Disposition of Money.

Except as otherwise provided by law, the Commission shall pay all money collected under this title into the General Fund of the State.

§ 8-214. Authority of Secretary.

The Commission exercises its powers and performs its duties subject to the authority of the Secretary.

Subtitle 3. Licensing

§ 8-301. License Required; Exceptions.

(a) Except as otherwise provided in this title, a person must have a contractor license whenever the person acts as a contractor in the State.

(b) Except as otherwise provided in this title, a person must have a subcontractor license or contractor license whenever the person acts as a subcontractor in the State.

(c) Except as otherwise provided in this title, a person must have a salesperson license or contractor license whenever the person sells a home improvement in the State.

(d) This section does not apply to:

(1) an individual who works for a contractor or subcontractor for a salary or wages but who is not a salesperson for the contractor;

(2) a clerical employee, retail clerk, or other employee of a licensed contractor who is not a salesperson, as to a transaction on the premises of the licensed contractor;

(3) a solicitor for a contractor who calls an owner by telephone only;

(4) an architect, electrician, plumber, heating, ventilation, air-conditioning, or refrigeration contractor, or other person who:

(i) is required by State or local law to meet standards of competency or experience before engaging in an occupation or profession;

(ii) currently is licensed in that occupation or profession under State or local law; and

(iii) is:

1. acting only within the scope of that occupation or profession; or

2. installing a central heating or air-conditioning system;

(5) a security systems technician licensed under Title 18 of the Business Occupations and Professions Article; or

(6) a person who is selling a home improvement to be performed by a person described in item (4) of this subsection.

§ 8-302. Examinations.

(a) An applicant for a contractor's, subcontractor's, or salesperson's license must pass the examination prior to submitting an application for a license.

(b) An applicant may receive a license only if the applicant passes the examination that the Commission requires.

(c) (1) To take an examination, an applicant shall pay to the Commission or a testing service chosen by the Commission the examination fee set by the Commission to cover the cost of the examination.

(2) The examination fee is nonrefundable.

(d) (1) The Commission shall schedule the applicant for an examination to be held within 45 days after the Commission receives an application for examination.

(2) The examination shall be held at a location:

(i) that is within the general geographic area where the applicant resides, if the applicant resides in the State; or

(ii) that the Commission determines, if the applicant resides out of State.

(e) The Commission shall give each qualified applicant notice of the time and place of examination.

(f) (1) Except as otherwise provided in this section, the Commission shall determine the subjects, scope, and form of and the passing score for examinations.

(2) The examination shall test:

(i) the applicant's knowledge of the law about home improvement; and

(ii) the applicant's competency to engage in the licensed occupation.

(3) The competency part of the examination may be oral or written.

(g) (1) The Commission may use a testing service to administer the examinations given under this section.

(2) If the Commission uses a testing service under this subsection, the testing service, subject to the requirements set by the Commission, may:

(i) set the time and place of examinations;

(ii) give qualified applicants notice of the time and place of examinations; and

(iii) furnish any other information that the Commission may require the testing service to provide.

(h) Within 30 days after the first meeting of the Commission after an examination date, the Commission shall notify an applicant in writing of the examination score of the applicant. (NOTE: This subsection effective October 1, 2004.)

§ 8-302.1. Contractor License – Liability Insurance. (Effective October 1, 2002)

(a) An applicant for a contractor license shall maintain general liability insurance in the amount of at least $50,000.

(b) A licensed contractor shall maintain general liability insurance in the amount of at least $50,000.

§ 8-302.2. Same – Qualifications of Applicants.

An applicant for a contractor license shall have:

(1) at least 2 years of trade experience that is satisfactory to the Commission, under regulations adopted by the Commission; or

(2) comparable educational training to be determined by regulations adopted by the Commission.

§ 8-303. Applications for Licenses.

(a) (1) An applicant for a license shall:

(i) submit to the Commission an application on the form that the Commission provides;

(ii) submit to the Commission with the license application proof of compliance with the insurance requirement of § 8-302.1 of this subtitle, if the applicant is applying for a contractor license;

(iii) pay into the Fund the fee required under § 8-404(a) of this title, if the applicant is applying for a contractor license; and

(iv) pay to the Commission an application fee.

(2) The application fee:

(i) for a contractor license is $225 for each place of business of the contractor;

(ii) for a subcontractor license is $125; or

(iii) for a salesperson license is $75.

(3) To cover the cost of processing an application, $15 of the application fee is nonrefundable.

(b) In addition to any other information required on an application form, the form shall require:

(1) for an individual applicant, the name and address of the applicant;

(2) for a corporate applicant, the name and address of each officer;

(3) for a partnership applicant, the name and address of each partner;

(4) for a joint venture applicant, the name and address of each party to the joint venture;

(5) if the applicant acts as a contractor or subcontractor through a corporation or limited partnership, the name and address of the resident agent of the corporation or limited partnership in the State;

(6) if the applicant is applying for a contractor license or subcontractor license, a complete description of the nature of the contracting business of the applicant;

(7) if the applicant is applying for a salesperson license, a complete description of the duties of the applicant;

(8) a record of the applicant's experience in the field of home improvement or other construction work, including dates when and addresses where the applicant has resided and done business;

(9) whether the applicant has ever held a professional or vocational license in this or any other state; and

(10) whether the applicant has had a professional or vocational license denied, suspended, or revoked.

(c) To evaluate the qualifications of an applicant for a license, the Commission may ask the applicant for:

(1) information about the applicant's character, experience, and financial stability; and

(2) any other information that the Commission needs.

(d) If the applicant is applying for a contractor license, the applicant shall:

(1) have submitted to the Commission, by a credit reporting agency approved by the Commission, a credit report that contains the information required by the Commission; or

(2) have paid to the Commission or the Commission's designee a credit report fee in an amount not to exceed the cost charged by a credit reporting agency approved by the Commission to obtain a credit report that contains the information required by the Commission.

(e) Financial information that an applicant submits to the Commission:

(1) is confidential and is not a public record; but

(2) if relevant, is admissible as evidence in an administrative or judicial proceeding.

(f) Notwithstanding subsection (a) of this section, an applicant that is incorporated or has its principal office in another state shall pay to the Commission the fee imposed in that state on a similar nonresident business if that fee is higher than the application fee under subsection (a) of this section.

§ 8-305. Approval or Denial of License.

(a) Within 30 days after the first meeting of the Commission after submission of a completed application, the Commission shall notify an applicant in writing:

(1) whether the application for a license is approved or denied; and

(2) of the reasons for denial, if the application is denied.

(NOTE: This subsection effective October 1, 2004.)

(b) (1) If the application is denied, the applicant, within 10 days after the notice of denial is mailed, may request a hearing.

(2) The hearing shall be held in accordance with § 8-312 of this subtitle within 30 days after the date that the Commission receives the request.

(3) The Commission shall make a decision within a reasonable time, but not later than 60 days after the hearing.

§ 8-306. Issuance of License.

(a) The Commission shall issue a license to each applicant who meets the requirements of this subtitle.

(b) The Commission:

(1) may issue a salesperson license only to an individual; and

(2) may not issue a salesperson license unless the Commission has received from a licensed contractor written notice, signed by both the licensed contractor and salesperson, of an employment or other contractual relationship between the licensed contractor and salesperson.

(c) Except as otherwise provided in subsection (d) of this section, the Commission may not issue a license to an applicant for a contractor license, subcontractor license, or salesperson license who has been convicted of violating § 8-601 of this title.

(d) The Commission may issue a contractor license, subcontractor license, or salesperson license to an applicant who has been convicted of violating § 8-601 of this title if:

(1) the Commission determines that the applicant has settled all outstanding obligations; and

(2) 1 year has passed since the date of conviction.

(e) The Commission may not issue a contractor license to an applicant unless the applicant has submitted to the Commission proof of compliance with the insurance requirement of § 8-302.1 of this subtitle.

§ 8-307. Scope of License.

(a) A contractor license authorizes the licensee to act as a contractor or subcontractor and to sell a home improvement.

(b) A subcontractor license authorizes the licensee to act as a subcontractor.

(c) A salesperson license authorizes the licensee to sell a home improvement.

(d) A license issued under this subtitle does not authorize the licensee to engage in a business or provide a service that may be engaged in or provided only by a person licensed under other State or local law.

§ 8-308. Term and Renewal of License.

(a) The Secretary may stagger the terms of licenses.

(b) Unless a license is renewed for a 2-year term as provided in this section, the license expires:

(1) if the Secretary staggers the terms of licenses, on the date that the Secretary sets; or

(2) if the Secretary does not stagger the terms of licenses, on the first June 30 that comes after the effective date of the license in an odd-numbered year.

(c) At least 1 month before a license expires, the Commission shall mail to the licensee, at the last known address of the licensee:

(1) a renewal application form; and

(2) a notice that states:

(i) the date on which the current license expires;

(ii) the date by which the Commission must receive the renewal application for the renewal to be issued and mailed before the license expires; and

(iii) the amount of the renewal fee.

(d) (1) Before a license expires, the licensee periodically may renew it for an additional 2-year term, if the licensee:

(i) otherwise is entitled to be licensed;

(ii) submits to the Commission a renewal application on the form that the Commission provides;

(iii) submits to the Commission proof of compliance with the insurance requirement of § 8-302.1 of this subtitle, if the licensee is renewing a contractor license; and

(iv) pays to the Commission a renewal fee.

(2) The renewal fee:

(i) for a contractor license is $225 for each place of business of the contractor;

(ii) for a subcontractor license is $125; or

(iii) for a salesperson license is $75.

(3) Notwithstanding paragraph (2) of this subsection, a licensee that is incorporated or has its principal office in another state shall pay to the Commission the fee imposed in that state on a similar nonresident business if that fee is higher than the renewal fee under paragraph (2) of this subsection.

(e) For renewal of a contractor license, the licensee shall:

(1) submit to the Commission, by a credit reporting agency approved by the Commission, a credit report that contains the information required by the Commission; or

(2) pay to the Commission or the Commission's designee a credit report fee in an amount not to exceed the cost charged by a credit reporting agency approved by the Commission to obtain a credit report that contains the information required by the Commission for renewal of a contractor license.

(f) (1) The Commission shall renew the license of each licensee who meets the requirements of this section.

(2) The Commission may not renew a contractor license unless the contractor submits proof of compliance with the insurance requirement of § 8-302.1 of this subtitle.

(g) A licensed contractor shall give the Commission notice of the cancellation of insurance required under Section 8-302.1 of this subtitle at least 10 days before the effective date of cancellation.

§ 8-308.1. Inactive Status.

(a) The Commission shall place the license of a licensee on inactive status, and issue an inactive status certificate to the licensee, if the licensee:

(1) submits to the Commission an application for inactive status on the form that the Commission provides;

(2) pays to the Commission an inactive status application fee not exceeding $50, as set by the Commission;

(3) except for the liability insurance requirement of § 8-302.1 of this subtitle, qualifies for an active license; and

(4) returns the license of the licensee to the Commission.

(b) (1) The holder of a contractor license that is on inactive status may not act as a contractor in the State.

(2) The holder of a subcontractor license that is on inactive status may not act as a subcontractor in the State.

(3) The holder of a salesperson license that is on inactive status may not sell a home improvement in the State.

(c) (1) The holder of a contractor license that is on inactive status is not required to meet the liability insurance requirement of § 8-302.1 of this subtitle.

(2) The holder of a contractor license that is on inactive status is not subject to an assessment for the Fund under § 8-404(b) of this subtitle.

(d) The placement of a license on inactive status does not affect the power of the Commission to suspend or revoke the license or to take any other disciplinary action against the licensee.

(e) (1) A licensee whose license is on inactive status remains responsible for renewing the license as required under § 8-308 of this subtitle.

(2) The holder of a contractor license that is on inactive status may renew the license without complying with the liability insurance requirement of § 8-302.1 of this subtitle.

(3) Notwithstanding § 8-308 of this subtitle, a licensee whose license is on inactive status shall pay to the Commission a renewal fee of:

(i) $112.50 for a contractor license;

(ii) $62.50 for a subcontractor license; or

(iii) $37.50 for a salesperson license.

(f) The Commission shall reactivate the license of a licensee that is on inactive status and reissue the license to the licensee, if the licensee:

(1) submits to the Commission an application for reactivation on the form that the Commission provides;

(2) pays to the Commission a reissuance fee of $10; and

(3) meets the requirements for a license, including, in the case of a contractor, the liability insurance requirement under § 8-302.1 of this subtitle.

§ 8-309. Change of Information.

Within 10 days, a licensee shall notify the Commission of a change of control in ownership, management, address, or trade name.

§ 8-310. Relationship of Salespersons and Contractors.

(a) A salesperson may not represent more than 2 contractors at a time.

(b) Before an individual becomes a salesperson for a contractor, the individual shall tell:

(1) that contractor the name of each other contractor for whom the individual currently is a salesperson; and

(2) each contractor for whom the individual currently is a salesperson the name of the contractor for whom the individual plans to become a salesperson.

(c) When an individual ceases to be a salesperson for a contractor, the contractor shall give the Commission written notice of the cessation.

§ 8-311. Denials, Repimands, Suspensions, and Revocations – Grounds, Penalty.

(a) Subject to the hearing provisions of § 8-312 of this subtitle, the Commission may deny a license to an applicant, reprimand a licensee, or suspend or revoke a license if the applicant or licensee or the management personnel of the applicant or licensee:

(1) fraudulently or deceptively obtains or attempts to obtain a license for the applicant or licensee or for another person;

(2) fraudulently or deceptively uses a license;

(3) fails to give the Commission information required by this subtitle about an application for a license;

(4) fails to pass an examination required by this subtitle;

(5) under the laws of the United States or of any state, is convicted of a:

(i) felony; or

(ii) misdemeanor that is directly related to the fitness and qualification of the applicant or licensee to engage in home improvement services;

(6) often fails to perform home improvement contracts;

(7) falsifies an account;

(8) engages in fraud;

(9) as a contractor or subcontractor fails to show financial solvency, based on the intended scope and size of the business in relation to total assets, liabilities, credit rating, and net worth;

(10) as a contractor or subcontractor lacks competence, as shown by the performance of an unworkmanlike, inadequate, or incomplete home improvement;

(11) violates this title;

(12) attempts to violate this title; or

(13) violates a regulation adopted under this title.

(b) Subject to the hearing provisions of § 8-312 of this subtitle, the Commission may reprimand a contractor or subcontractor or suspend or revoke the license of a contractor or subcontractor for a violation of this title by an agent, director, employee, manager, officer, partner, or salesperson of the contractor or subcontractor, unless the Commission finds that the contractor or subcontractor or management personnel of the contractor or subcontractor:

(1) had no knowledge of the wrongful conduct; or

(2) could not prevent the violation.

(c) Instead of or in addition to reprimanding a licensee or suspending or revoking a license, the Commission may impose a civil penalty under § 8-620 of this title.

(d) The Commission shall consider the following facts in the granting, denial, renewal, suspension, or revocation of a license or the reprimand of a licensee when an applicant or licensee is convicted of a felony or misdemeanor described in subsection (a)(5) of this section:

(1) the nature of the crime;

(2) the relationship of the crime to the activities authorized by the license;

(3) with respect to a felony, the relevance of the conviction to the fitness and qualification of the applicant or licensee to provide home improvement services;

(4) the length of time since the conviction; and

(5) the behavior and activities of the applicant or licensee before and after the conviction.

§ 8-312. Same – Hearings.

(a) Except as otherwise provided in § 10-226 of the State Government Article, before the Commission takes any final action under § 8-311 of this subtitle, it shall give the person against whom the action is contemplated an opportunity for a hearing before the Commission or, as provided under § 8-313 of this subtitle, a hearing board.

(b) The Commission shall give notice and hold the hearing in accordance with Title 10, Subtitle 2 of the State Government Article.

(c) The Commission may administer oaths in a proceeding under this section.

(d) The hearing notice to be given to the person shall be sent at least 10 days before the hearing by certified mail to the business address of the licensee on record with the Commission.

(e) (1) For purposes of this subsection, the State is divided into:

(i) the region that includes Allegany, Carroll, Frederick, Garrett, and Washington Counties;

(ii) the region that includes Anne Arundel, Calvert, Charles, and St. Mary's Counties;

(iii) the region that includes Baltimore City and Baltimore and Howard Counties;

(iv) the region that includes Caroline, Cecil, Dorchester, Harford, Kent, Queen Anne's, Somerset, Talbot, Wicomico, and Worcester Counties; and

(v) the region that includes Montgomery and Prince George's Counties.

(2) The Commission shall set the time and place of the hearing but shall hold the hearing in the appropriate region to accommodate the needs of:

(i) disabled witnesses;

(ii) indigent witnesses; or

(iii) a majority of witnesses.

(f) The person may be represented at the hearing by counsel.

(g) In connection with a proceeding under this section, the Commission may:

(1) issue subpoenas for the attendance of witnesses to testify or to produce evidence; and

(2) take testimony in the same manner and with the same fees and compensation for mileage as provided in civil cases in the State.

(h) If, after due notice, the person against whom the action is contemplated does not appear, nevertheless the Commission may hear and determine the matter.

§ 8-313. Home Improvement Hearing Board.

(a) With the approval of the Secretary, the Commission may appoint a home improvement hearing board.

(b) (1) A hearing board shall consist of at least 3 members of the Commission.

(2) Of the members of the hearing board:

(i) at least 1 shall have experience in some phase of the business of home improvement; and

(ii) at least 1 shall be a consumer member of the Commission.

(c) The Commission shall appoint a chairman from among the members of the hearing board.

(d) The Commission may refer to a hearing board a charge, claim, complaint, or license application made by the Commission or by any person under this subtitle.

(e) Each procedure applicable to a hearing before the Commission is applicable to a hearing before the hearing board.

(f) (1) A decision of the hearing board shall be:

(i) by a majority vote of the entire membership of the hearing board;

(ii) in writing; and

(iii) submitted to the Commission.

(2) Unless, within 15 days after the hearing board submits its decision to the Commission, the Commission or a member of the Commission finds that a full hearing by the Commission is required:

    (i) the decision of the hearing board is final;

    (ii) the decision is a final decision of the Commission; and

    (iii) a party who is aggrieved by the decision may take an appeal as provided in § 8-314 of this subtitle.

§ 8-314. Judicial Review.

A party to a proceeding before the Commission who is aggrieved by a final decision of the Commission in a contested case, as defined in § 10-202 of the State Government Article, may take an appeal as allowed in §§ 10-222 and 10-223 of the State Government Article.

§ 8-315. Payment of Compensation; Effect of Loss of License.

(a) Except as otherwise provided in subsection (b) of this section, a contractor or subcontractor may not pay or otherwise compensate another contractor or subcontractor or a salesperson for performing or selling a home improvement unless:

    (1) the person to be paid or compensated is licensed;

    (2) the person to be paid or compensated is not subject to the licensing requirements of this title; or

    (3) the transaction for which the consideration is to be paid is not subject to this title.

(b) After the expiration, suspension, or revocation of a license, a person:

    (1) is not relieved of outstanding obligations; and

    (2) may complete and be paid under a home improvement contract that is made but not performed on the date of the expiration, suspension, or revocation.

§ 8-316. Reapplication for License, Reinstatement of License.

(a) A person may not reapply for a license within 6 months after the person has had a license:

    (1) denied after a hearing; or

    (2) revoked.

(b) The Commission may reinstate the license of a person whose license has been suspended or revoked under this subtitle only if the person passes the examination that the Commission requires.

§ 8-317. Construction License.

A contractor or subcontractor who holds a license under this title is not required to hold a construction license under Title 17 of this article.

Subtitle 4. Home Improvement Guaranty Fund.

§ 8-401. "Actual Loss" Defined.

In this subtitle, "actual loss" means the costs of restoration, repair, replacement, or completion that arise from an unworkmanlike, inadequate, or incomplete home improvement.

§ 8-402. Scope of Subtitle.

This subtitle does not:

(1) limit the authority of the Commission to take disciplinary action against a licensee under Subtitle 3 of this title;

(2) limit the availability of other remedies to a claimant; or

(3) require a claimant to exhaust administrative remedies before the Commission before bringing an action in court.

§ 8-403. Establishment; Disposition of Money; Investments; Administration.

(a) The Commission shall:

(1) establish a Home Improvement Guaranty Fund; and

(2) keep the Fund at a level of at least $250,000.

(b) (1) The Commission shall deposit all money collected to the credit of the Fund with the State Treasurer for placement in a special account.

(2) (i) The State Treasurer shall invest the money in the Fund in the same way that money in the State Retirement and Pension System is invested.

(ii) Investment earnings shall be credited to the Fund.

(c) The Commission shall administer the Fund in accordance with this subtitle.

§ 8-404. Initial fee; Assessments.

(a) Before the Commission issues a contractor license, the contractor shall pay a fee of $100 to be credited to the Fund.

(b) (1) If the Commission finds that, because of pending claims, the amount of the Fund may fall below $250,000, the Commission shall assess each contractor a fee of $50.

(2) However, under this subsection the Commission may not assess a contractor more than $150 in a calendar year.

(c) If a contractor fails to pay an assessment within 60 days after notice of the assessment, the contractor license is suspended until the assessment is paid.

§ 8-405. Claims Against Fund.

(a) Subject to this subtitle, an owner may recover compensation from the Fund for an actual loss that results from an act or omission by a licensed contractor or a violation of § 8-607(4) of this title as found by the Commission or a court of competent jurisdiction.

(b) For purposes of recovery from the Fund, the act or omission of a licensed contractor includes the act or omission of a subcontractor, salesperson, or employee of the licensed contractor, whether or not an express agency relationship exists.

(c) A claimant shall comply with a written agreement to submit a dispute to arbitration before seeking recovery from the Fund.

(d) The Commission may deny a claim if the Commission finds that the claimant unreasonably rejected good faith efforts by the contractor to resolve the claim.

(e) The Commission may not award from the Fund:

(1) more than $15,000 to 1 claimant for acts or omissions of 1 contractor;

(2) more than $100,000 to all claimants for acts or omissions of 1 contractor unless, after the Commission has paid out $100,000 on account of acts or omissions of the contractor, the contractor reimburses $100,000 to the Fund;

(3) an amount for attorney fees, consequential damages, court costs, interest, personal injury damages, or punitive damages; or

(4) an amount as a result of a default judgment in court.

(f) (1) A claim against the Fund based on the act or omission of a particular contractor may not be made by:

(i) a spouse or other immediate relative of the contractor;

(ii) an employee, officer, or partner of the contractor; or

(iii) an immediate relative of an employee, officer, or partner of the contractor.

(2) An owner may make a claim against the Fund only if the owner:

(i) resides in the home as to which the claim is made; or

(ii) does not own more than 3 residences or dwelling places.

(g) A claim shall be brought against the Fund within 3 years after the claimant discovered or, by use of ordinary diligence, should have discovered the loss or damage.

§ 8-406. Procedure for Submitting Claims.

To begin a proceeding to recover from the Fund, a claimant shall submit to the Commission a claim, under oath, that states:

(1) the amount claimed based on the actual loss;

(2) the facts giving rise to the claim;

(3) any other evidence that supports the claim; and

(4) any other information that the Commission requires.

§ 8-407. Action on Claim by Commission.

(a) The procedures for notice, hearings, and judicial review that apply to proceedings under Subtitle 3 of this title also apply to proceedings to recover from the Fund.

(b) On receipt of a claim, the Commission shall:

(1) send a copy of the claim to the contractor alleged to be responsible for the actual loss; and

(2) require a written response to the claim within 10 days.

(c) (1) The Commission:

(i) shall review the claim and any response to it; and

(ii) may investigate the claim.

(2) On the basis of its review and any investigation, the Commission may:

(i) set the matter for a hearing;

(ii) dismiss the claim, if the claim is frivolous, legally insufficient, or made in bad faith; or

(iii) issue a proposed order to pay all or part of the claim or deny the claim if the total claim against a particular contractor does not exceed $2,500.

(d) (1) The Commission shall send the proposed order to the claimant and the contractor, at the most recent address on record with the Commission, by:

(i) personal delivery; or

(ii) both regular mail and certified mail, return receipt requested.

(2) Within 21 days after service, receipt, or attempted delivery of the proposed order, the claimant or contractor may submit to the Commission:

(i) a written request for a hearing before the Commission; or

(ii) a written exception to the proposed order.

(3) If the claimant or contractor submits a timely exception to the proposed order, the Commission may:

(i) issue a revised proposed order;

(ii) set a hearing on the claim; or

(iii) dismiss the claim.

(4) Unless the claimant or contractor submits a timely request for a hearing or a timely exception, the proposed order is final.

(e) (1) At a hearing on a claim, the claimant has the burden of proof.

(2) If a subcontractor or salesperson is necessary to adjudicate a claim fairly, the Commission shall issue a subpoena for that person to appear at the hearing.

§ 8-408. Joinder of Proceedings; Administrative and Legal Proceedings.

(a) (1) The Commission may join a proceeding on a claim against the Fund with a disciplinary proceeding against a licensed contractor under Subtitle 3 of this title, if the disciplinary hearing is based on the same facts alleged in the claim.

(2) In a consolidated proceeding, the claimant is a party and may participate in the hearing to the extent necessary to establish the claim.

(b) (1) Notwithstanding § 8-402(2) of this subtitle, a claimant may not concurrently submit a claim to recover from the Fund and bring an action in a court of competent jurisdiction against a contractor based on the same facts alleged in the claim.

(2) If the claimant brings an action in a court of competent jurisdiction based on the same facts alleged in a pending claim, the Commission shall stay its proceedings on the claim until there is a final judgment and all rights to appeal are exhausted.

(3) (i) To the extent that a final judgment or final award in arbitration is decided in favor of the claimant, the Commission shall approve the claim against the Fund.

(ii) If a final judgment or final award in arbitration is decided in favor of the defendant, the Commission shall dismiss the claim against the Fund.

§ 8-409. Payments From Fund.

(a) The Commission may order payment of a claim against the Fund only if:

(1) the decision or order of the Commission is final in accordance with Title 10, Subtitle 2 of the State Government Article and all rights of appeal are exhausted; or

(2) the claimant provides the Commission with a certified copy of a final judgment of a court of competent jurisdiction or a final award in arbitration, with all rights of appeal exhausted, in which the court or arbitrator:

(i) expressly has found on the merits that the claimant is entitled to recover under § 8-405(a) of this subtitle; and

(ii) has found the value of the actual loss.

(b) (1) Except as otherwise provided in this subsection, the Commission shall pay approved claims in the order submitted.

(2) If approved claims submitted to the Commission against a contractor exceed $100,000 less the amount of unreimbursed claim payments previously made for the contractor, the Commission may pay the approved claims proportionately so that each claimant receives the same percentage payment of the claims.

(3) After the Fund is reimbursed, the Commission shall pay unsatisfied approved claims.

(c) If there is not enough money in the Fund to pay an approved claim wholly or partly, the Commission shall pay the unpaid claim:

(1) when enough money is deposited in the Fund; and

(2) in the order that each claim originally was filed with a court of competent jurisdiction or submitted to the Commission.

§ 8-410. Reimbursement of Fund.

(a) (1) After the Commission pays a claim from the Fund:

(i) the Commission is subrogated to all rights of the claimant in the claim up to the amount paid;

(ii) the claimant shall assign to the Commission all rights of the claimant in the claim up to the amount paid; and

(iii) the Commission has a right to reimbursement of the Fund by the contractor who the Commission finds responsible for the act or omission giving rise to the claim for:

1. the amount paid from the Fund; and

2. interest on that amount at an annual rate of at least 10%, as set by the Commission.

(2) All money that the Commission recovers on a claim shall be deposited in the Fund.

(b) If, within 30 days after the Commission gives notice, a contractor on whose account a claim was paid does not reimburse the Fund in full, the Commission may sue the contractor in a court of competent jurisdiction for the unreimbursed amount.

(c) The Commission is entitled to a judgment for the unreimbursed amount if the Commission proves that:

(1) a claim was paid from the Fund on account of the contractor;

(2) the contractor has not reimbursed the Fund in full;

(3) the contractor was given notice and an opportunity to participate in a hearing on the claim before the Commission; and

(4) (i) the Commission directed payment based on a final judgment of a court of competent jurisdiction or a final award in arbitration; or

(ii) the decision or order of the Commission is final in accordance with Title 10, Subtitle 2 of the State Government Article and there is no pending appeal.

(d) The Commission may refer to the Central Collection Unit for collection under §§ 13-912 through 13-919 of the Tax - General Article a debt owed to the Commission by a contractor on whose account a claim was paid from the Fund and who is at least 1 year behind in reimbursement payments to the Fund.

(e) For the purpose of excepting to a discharge of a contractor under federal bankruptcy law, the Commission is a creditor of the contractor for the amount paid from the Fund.

(f) (1) (i) If a person liable for reimbursing the Guaranty Fund under this section receives a demand for reimbursement and fails to reimburse the Fund, the reimbursement amount and any accrued interest or cost are a lien in favor of the State on any real property of the person if the lien is recorded and indexed as provided in this subsection.

(ii) Interest shall continue at the rate of interest on a judgment as provided in § 11-107(a) of the Courts Article until the full amount due the Fund is paid.

(2) The lien in favor of the State created by this subsection may not attach to specific property until the State Central Collection Unit records written notice of the lien in the office of the clerk of the court for the county in which the property subject to the lien or any part of the property is located.

(3) The lien in favor of the State created by this subsection does not have priority as to any specific property over any person who is a lienholder of record at the time the notice required under paragraph (2) of this subsection is recorded.

(4) The notice required under paragraph (2) of this subsection shall contain:

(i) the name and address of the person against whose property the lien exists;

(ii) the amount of the lien;

(iii) a description of or reference to the property subject to the lien; and

(iv) the date the Guaranty Fund paid the claim giving rise to the lien.

(5) Upon presentation of a release of any lien in favor of the State created by this subsection, the clerk of the court in which the lien is recorded and indexed shall record and index the release and shall note in the lien docket the date the release is filed and the fact that the lien is released.

(6) The notice required under paragraph (2) of this subsection and any release filed under paragraph (5) of this subsection shall be indexed with the judgment lien records maintained by the office of the clerk of the court where the notice is recorded.

(7) The clerk may collect a reasonable fee for recording and indexing each notice of lien or release of any lien under this subsection.

§ 8-411. Disciplinary Proceedings.

(a) Except as provided in subsection (b) of this section, if the Commission pays a claim against the Fund based on an act or omission of a contractor, the Commission may suspend the contractor license until the contractor reimburses the Fund in full for:

(1) the amount paid from the Fund; and

(2) interest on that amount at an annual rate of at least 10%, as set by the Commission.

(b) The Commission may not suspend the contractor license if the Commission finds that the contractor or management personnel of the contractor:

(1) did not know of the wrongful conduct; or

(2) could not prevent the violation.

(c) Reimbursement of the Fund in full by a contractor, by itself, does not nullify or modify the effect of a disciplinary proceeding against a licensee.

Subtitle 5. Miscellaneous Provisions.

§ 8-501. Home Improvement Contracts.

(a) A home improvement contract that does not comply with this section is not invalid merely because of noncompliance.

(b) Each home improvement contract shall:

(1) be in writing and legible;

(2) describe clearly each document that it incorporates; and

(3) be signed by each party to the home improvement contract.

(c) (1) In addition to any other matters on which the parties lawfully agree, each home improvement contract shall contain:

(i) the name, address, and license number of the contractor;

(ii) the name and license number of each salesperson who solicited the home improvement contract or sold the home improvement;

(iii) the approximate dates when the performance of the home improvement will begin and when it will be substantially completed;

(iv) a description of the home improvement to be performed and the materials to be used;

(v) the agreed consideration;

(vi) the number of monthly payments and the amount of each payment, including any finance charge;

(vii) a description of any collateral security for the obligation of the owner under the home improvement contract; and

(viii) a notice that gives the telephone number of the Commission and states that:

1. each contractor and each subcontractor must be licensed by the Commission; and

2. anyone may ask the Commission about a contractor or subcontractor.

(2) If payment for work performed under the home improvement contract will be secured by an interest in residential real estate, a written notice in not smaller than 10 point bold type that is on the first page of the contract shall state in substantially the following form: "This contract creates a mortgage or lien against your property to secure payment and may cause a loss of your property if you fail to pay the amount agreed upon. You have the right to consult an attorney. You have the right to rescind this contract within 3 business days after the date you sign it by notifying the contractor in writing that you are rescinding the contract."

(3) The notice under paragraph (2) of this subsection shall be independently initialed by the homeowner.

(d) Before the performance of a home improvement begins, the owner shall be given a copy of the home improvement contract signed by the contractor.

(e) A salesperson or other agent or employee of a contractor may not make a change in a home improvement contract for an owner.

§ 8-502. Conduct of Salespersons.

(a) A salesperson may not:

(1) represent concurrently more than 1 contractor in selling a home improvement;

(2) use a home improvement contract form that does not disclose the name of the contractor; or

(3) choose a contractor for an owner.

(b) For selling a home improvement, a salesperson shall:

(1) accept compensation only from the contractor that the salesperson represents in the sale; and

(2) pay compensation only for that contractor.

§ 8-503. Inducements.

(a) As an inducement to make a home improvement contract, a person may not promise or offer to pay to an owner any compensation or reward for obtaining or placing home improvement business with others.

(b) A contractor or salesperson may not offer, give, or pay to an owner a gift, bonus award, merchandise, trading stamps, or cash loan as an inducement to make a home improvement contract.

(c) To advertise or to promote sales, a contractor or salesperson may give to a prospective customer a tangible item if:

    (1) The cost to the contractor or salesperson does not exceed $25;

    (2) the gift is not contingent on making a home improvement contract; and

    (3) the customer does not receive more than 1 item for 1 transaction.

§ 8-504. Permits.

Except for a permit for a home improvement to be performed by a property owner, the building and permits department of a county or a municipal corporation may not issue a permit for a home improvement unless the permit includes the license number of a licensed contractor.

§ 8-505. Notice of Building Code Violations.

(a) In this section, "building code" includes a code that deals with mechanical, electrical, fire, plumbing, energy, heating, ventilation, or air conditioning matters.

(b) A county or municipal corporation shall notify the Commission of each contractor who fails to correct a violation of the applicable local or State building code within a reasonable time after the contractor receives notice of the violation.

Subtitle 6. Prohibited Acts; Penalties

Part 1. Specific Prohibited Acts and Specific Penalties.

§ 8-601. Acting as Contractor or Subcontractor or Selling a Home Improvement without License.

(a) Except as otherwise provided in this title, a person may not act or offer to act as a contractor in the State unless the person has a contractor license.

(b) Except as otherwise provided in this title, a person may not act or offer to act as a subcontractor in the State unless the person has a contractor license or subcontractor license.

(c) Except as otherwise provided in this title, a person may not sell or offer to sell a home improvement in the State unless the person has a contractor license or salesperson license.

(d) A person who violates this section is guilty of a misdemeanor and, on first conviction, is subject to a fine not exceeding $1,000 or imprisonment not exceeding 30 days or both and, on a second or subsequent conviction, is subject to a fine not exceeding $5,000 or imprisonment not exceeding 2 years or both.

§ 8-602. False Proof of Completion.

(a) A person may not accept a completion certificate or other proof that performance of a home improvement contract is complete or satisfactorily concluded with knowledge that the document or proof is false and the performance is incomplete.

(b) If a person knows or has good reason to know that a completion certificate or other proof is false, the person may not utter, offer, or use the document or proof to:

(1) make or accept an assignment or negotiation of the right to receive payment from an owner under a home improvement contract; or

(2) get or grant credit or a loan on the security of the right to receive payment under a home improvement contract.

(c) A person who violates this section is guilty of a misdemeanor and, on conviction, is subject to a fine not exceeding $5,000 or imprisonment not exceeding 3 years or both.

Part II. Miscellaneous Prohibited Acts.

§ 8-605. Abandonment of or Failure to Perform Contract.

A contractor may not:

(1) abandon or fail to perform, without justification, a home improvement contract; or

(2) deviate materially from plans or specifications without the consent of the owner.

§ 8-606. Failure to Account for or Remit Payment.

A salesperson may not fail to account for or remit to the contractor whom the salesperson represents a payment received in connection with selling a home improvement.

§ 8-607. Misrepresentation.

A person may not:

(1) make a substantial misrepresentation when obtaining a home improvement contract;

(2) make a false promise that is likely to influence, persuade, or induce in connection with a home improvement contract;

(3) misrepresent a material fact when applying for a license; or

(4) fail to give the written notice required under § 8-501(c)(2) and (3) of this title.

§ 8-608. Fraud.

A person may not commit fraud when executing or materially altering a home improvement contract, mortgage, promissory note, or other document incident to performing or selling a home improvement.

§ 8-609. Debt Limitation.

A person may not prepare, arrange, accept, or participate in arranging a mortgage, promissory note, or other evidence of debt for performing or selling a home improvement with knowledge that the evidence of debt states a greater monetary obligation than the consideration, including a time sale price, for the home improvement.

§ 8-610. False, Deceptive, or Misleading Advertising.

(a) A person may not:

(1) directly or indirectly publish a false, deceptive, or misleading advertisement about home improvement; or

(2) advertise or offer, by any means, to perform a home improvement if the person does not intend to accept a home improvement contract:

(i) to do the particular home improvement; or

(ii) at the price advertised or offered.

(b) An advertisement that is subject to and complies with regulations adopted by the Federal Trade Commission is not false, deceptive, or misleading.

§ 8-611. Violation of Laws.

A licensee may not violate:

(1) a building law of the State or a political subdivision of the State;

(2) a safety or labor law of the State; or

(3) the Maryland Workers' Compensation Act.

§ 8-612. Doing Business with Unlicensed Person.

A person may not perform or sell a home improvement with or through another person who is required to be licensed under this title but is not licensed.

§ 8-613. Failure to Notify Commission of Certain Changes.

A contractor may not fail to notify the Commission of an employment or other contractual relationship between the contractor and a salesperson.

§ 8-614. Conducting Business Under another Name.

A person may not act as a contractor or subcontractor or sell a home improvement under a name other than that under which the person is licensed.

§ 8-615. Advertising Without License Number.

A person may not advertise in any way that the person is licensed under this title unless the advertisement states the license number of the person in one of the following forms: "Maryland Home Improvement Commission License No. _____" or "MHIC No. _____".

§ 8-616. Failure to Comply with Order or Requirement.

A person may not fail to comply with a lawful order or requirement of the Commission under this title.

§ 8-617. Payment Before Signing Contract; Deposit Limited.

(a) A person may not demand or receive any payment for a home improvement before the home improvement contract is signed.

(b) A person may not receive a deposit of more than one-third of the home improvement contract price before or at the time of execution of the home improvement contract.

Part III. Civil Penalties

§ 8-620. Civil Penalties.

(a) The Commission may impose on a person who violates this title, including § 8-607(4) of this subtitle, a civil penalty not exceeding $5,000 for each violation, whether or not the person is licensed under this title.

(b) In setting the amount of a civil penalty, the Commission shall consider:

(1) the seriousness of the violation;

(2) the good faith of the violator;

(3) any previous violations;

(4) the harmful effect of the violation on the complainant, the public, and the business of home improvement;

(5) the assets of the violator; and

(6) any other relevant factors.

Part IV. General Criminal Penalty.

§ 8-623. General Criminal Penalty.

(a) This section only applies if there is no greater criminal penalty provided under this title or other applicable law.

(b) A person who violates this title is guilty of a misdemeanor and, on conviction, is subject to a fine not exceeding $1,000 or imprisonment not exceeding 6 months or both.

Subtitle 7. Short Title; Termination of Title.

§ 8-701. Short Title.

This title is the Maryland Home Improvement Law.

§ 8-702. Termination of Title.

Subject to the evaluation and reestablishment provisions of the Maryland Program Evaluation Act, this title and all regulations adopted under this title shall terminate on October 1, 2012.

APPENDIX B

CODE OF MARYLAND REGULATIONS

TITLE 09
SUBTITLE 08 HOME IMPROVEMENT COMMISSION

CHAPTER 01 GENERAL REGULATIONS

.01 Definitions.

The definitions contained in Business Regulation Article, § 8-101, Annotated Code of Maryland, are incorporated into these regulations, by reference, as Regulation .01.

.02 Definition of Canvasser, Solicitor.

The definitions of canvasser, solicitor, or similar term will be considered the same as the definition for a salesman; those persons using these terms will be subject to licensing and the requirements of the Maryland Home Improvement Law.

.03 Licenses for Contractors and Salesmen.

All contractors and salesmen required to be licensed shall have licenses on and after October 1, 1962.

.04 Corporate or Partnership Licensure.

A. A corporation or partnership may not act as a home improvement contractor unless it obtains a corporate or partnership home improvement contractor's license.

B. In order to obtain and maintain a corporate or partnership home improvement license, the corporation or partnership shall employ one individual licensed contractor who shall be in responsible charge of the corporation's or partnership's home improvement work.

C. The corporation or partnership and the individual in responsible charge of the corporation's or partnership's home improvement work shall be jointly and severally responsible for:

(1) Payment of any fees required by Business Regulation Article, §§8-302, 8-303, 8-308, and 8-404, Annotated Code of Maryland;

(2) Filing of a bond or other evidence of financial responsibility required by Business Regulation Article, §8-303(c), Annotated Code of Maryland;

(3) Repayment to the Home Improvement Commission Guaranty Fund pursuant to Business Regulation Article, §8-410, Annotated Code of Maryland, for any payments made to claimants from the Fund on account of violations by the corporation or partnership or the individual in responsible charge.

D. For purposes of applying the $100,000 limitation in Business Regulation Article, §8-405(e)(2), Annotated Code of Maryland, on Guaranty Fund awards on account of the conduct of any one licensed contractor, the combined liability of a licensed corporation or partnership and the individual in responsible charge of the corporation's or partnership's work may not exceed $100,000 in the aggregate.

E. The Commissions may, pursuant to Business Regulation Article, §8-311, Annotated Code of Maryland, sanction a corporation or partnership for conduct which is in violation of Business Regulation Article, Title 8, Annotated Code of Maryland.

.05 Issue of Salesman's License under Legal Name.

A salesman's license will be issued only in the legal name of the applicant for the license.

.06 License Numbers on Vehicles.

A. Licensed contractors and subcontractors shall conspicuously display their home improvement license number preceded by the designation "MHIC #' on both sides of all vehicles primarily used either by the licensee or under the licensee's direction and control for the performance of home improvement work.

B. For purposes of this regulation, performance of home improvement work:

(1) Shall include, but not be limited to, transporting materials to and from the jobsite;

(2) May not include sales work.

C. Contractors or subcontractors are required to display only their own license numbers while they are performing work as a subcontractor.

D. Displays required by this regulation shall be at least 3 inches in height.

.07 Salesman's Representation of Contractors.

A. A salesman may not represent any contractor unless the salesman complies with the provisions of this regulation.

B. A salesman seeking to represent any contractor shall make application on forms provided by the Commission.

C. A salesman may not represent more than two contractors at any one time.

D. Before the Commission may authorize a salesman to represent two contractors at the same time, the salesman shall provide to the Commission the following:

(1) Written notice of appointment or employment signed by both the contractor duly licensed with the Commission and the salesman; and

(2) A copy of notification by certified mail, and evidence of its receipt, to each contractor represented by the salesman stating the names and addresses of each contractor represented by the salesman.

E. A contractor shall promptly notify the Commission when his association with any salesman is terminated, and a salesman shall promptly return to the Commission any authorization issued by the Commission to represent the contractor.

.08 Duty of Prime Contractor on Home Improvement Contract.

In the performance of any Home Improvement Contract it shall be the non-delegable duty and obligation of the prime contractor to secure, or see to the securing of, every permit, license, or special exception necessary to the proper completion of the contract according to applicable state or local building laws.

.09 Advertising.

A.   General Requirements.

(1)   A licensed home improvement contractor may not solicit home improvement business by way of advertisement in a newspaper, magazine, circular, or printed document, or by way of television or radio announcement, unless the name and license number of the contractor are stated in the advertisement.

(2)   A licensee may not directly or indirectly publish any advertisement relating to home improvements, including finance or credit terms, that contains an assertion, representation, or statement of fact that is false, deceptive, or misleading.

(3)   General statements, such as "Factory to You", "Direct to You", "Buy from the Manufacturer", "Save the Middleman's Profit", or phrases of similar meaning may not be used unless the advertiser is actually the maker or producer of the merchandise advertised or offered for sale.

B.   Discount Coupons. An advertisement which offers a discount coupon may not contain a requirement that the coupon be presented before the contractor provides an estimate or proposal.

C.   Guaranties or Warranties.

(1)   If reference is made to a guaranty or warranty, or the word "guarantied" or "warranted" is used, the terms, conditions, limitations, and period of time covered shall be clearly and conspicuously disclosed. The terms shall indicate whether items such as "labor and material only," "repair," "replacement," or "full refund" are offered. Basic limitations shall be disclosed in the advertisement.

(2)   With respect to any guaranty offered by a licensee, compliance with the Maryland Consumer Products Guaranty Act, Commercial Law Article, §14-401—14-409, Annotated Code of Maryland, shall constitute prima facie evidence that a licensee has complied with §A(2) of this regulation. The Maryland Home Improvement Commission shall provide a copy of the Consumer Products Guaranty Act to any licensee within 5 days after receipt of a written request.

D.   Special Disclosure Requirements.

(1)   Credit Terms and Charges.

(a)   Statements and claims regarding installment buying plans, finance, credit service, and carrying or service charges, including references to down payments, amounts, and frequency of payments, shall be accurate and clearly understandable, made in good faith, and in compliance with all other statutes or regulations regulating installment contracts.

(b)   If a repayment price is offered, it shall be stated in specific amounts. The number of payments shall be stated, and the combination of amounts and number of payments advertised shall be readily available.

(2)   Prices.

(a)   If a price is stated in an advertisement which does not include all costs of items necessary for the proper function and appearance of the installed product, this shall be clearly and conspicuously qualified in conjunction with the stated price by an explanatory statement.

(b) When the price or specific credit terms are stated in an advertisement, the advertisement shall accurately describe what is being offered at that price or on those terms. Any limitations to, or conditions on, what will be supplied at the stated price or credit terms shall be clearly and conspicuously stated in immediate conjunction with the featured statement.

(c) If the price advertised does not include all of the accessories which either appear in the advertisement, or which are necessary to affect proper installation and proper use of the item, the advertisement shall state that fact clearly and prominently in immediate conjunction with the advertised price. Extra charges may not be used as a device to disguise the actual selling price of merchandise.

(3) Delivery Charges. If an extra charge is required to make delivery of an advertised home improvement item, it shall be clearly and conspicuously stated in the advertisement.

(4) Installation Charge. If installation is extra, the advertising shall disclose the fact clearly and conspicuously in immediate conjunction with the advertisement. For example:

(a) Installation Extra;

(b) Plus Installation;

(c) Installation at Extra Cost.

(5) Offer Not Valid in Maryland. A statement that an offer in an advertisement is not valid in Maryland shall be conspicuously displayed in the advertisement.

.10 Model Home Offers and Referral Offers.

A licensee may not promise to any owner that the owner's building will be used as a "model home," "advertising job," or for other similar purposes, when the licensee also will:

A. Pay a commission or other compensation to the owner for any sale made within any specified distance from the owner's building; or

B. Consequently reduce the cost for the owner of any home improvement work.

.11 Notice of Change of Licensing Information.

Licensees shall notify the Commission, in writing, within 10 days, of any change of control in ownership or management, or a change of address or trade name of the licensee. This notice shall be sent to the Executive Director of the Commission by certified mail, return receipt requested.

.12 Duty of Prime Contractor to Pay Subcontractors and Workmen.

In the performance of any home improvement contract, it shall be the nondelegable duty and obligation of the prime contractor to pay the subcontractors and workmen and materialmen so as to avoid the subjection of the property of the owner to mechanics' liens and materialmen's liens.

.13 Time Limitations for Filing Complaints.

The Commission may summarily dismiss any complaint brought against a licensee after 3 years from the date of the home improvement contract for the work from which the complaint arises, unless the Commission finds that the complainant's delay in bringing the complaint was justified and that the delay does not result in an undue burden for the licensee.

.14 Application for Licensure as Home Improvement Contractor.

An application for licensure as a home improvement contractor, whether it is in the name of an individual, partnership, proprietorship, or corporation, may not be accepted, if the name under which the licensee will be trading is the same as the name being used by an existing licensee, or is so similar to the name being used by an existing licensee that it will cause confusion on the part of the public at large. This regulation shall apply prospectively only to new applications received as of July 1, 1974.

.15 Contracts Subject to Approval of Licensee.

A.   Every home improvement contract which contains a stipulation or condition or which is represented to be that the contract is subject to the approval of the contractor before it becomes binding or any other language requiring prior approval before acceptance shall state that approval or disapproval of the contract shall be made within 10 working days from the date of the contract. The owner shall be duly informed, in writing, by the contractor of the decision approving or disapproving the contract within that time.

B.   If the home improvement contract described in §A of this regulation is not approved, money or other collateral tendered as a deposit or down payment to a contractor, salesman, or any other person shall be returned to the owner within 3 working days of the date of disapproval, and not later than 13 working days from the date of the contract.

.16 Examination.

A.   The examination shall be held as often as necessary at a test site determined by the Commission. This examination may be offered at various political subdivisions throughout the State. The examination shall include the law relating to the practice of home improvement contracting and the applicant's competence to perform home improvement work. The examination for competence may be oral or written.

B.   Each applicant shall file with the Commission a written application on forms which will be furnished on request. The application must be filed not later than 1 week before the date on which the examination is held, and must be accompanied by the required fee, and a full face photograph, taken within the year preceding the initial application.

C.   The passing mark shall be 70 in the subject matter. If the applicant has failed to pass the examination, he will not be eligible to reapply until 21 days have elapsed. A request for a second reconsideration received after the second failure will not be accepted until 60 days have elapsed.

D.   If an applicant fails to sit for the examination as scheduled, the applicant shall, in order to be rescheduled for the examination, file a written application, on forms provided by the Commission, accompanied by the fee as determined in Business Regulation Article, §8-302(c), Annotated Code of Maryland. The Commission may, for good cause and upon written request of the applicant, waive the requirement for a subsequent fee.

E.   The time limitation within which an applicant is required to pass is as stated in §C of this regulation. If an applicant has been denied registration of a license, because of failure to pass the examination, the applicant may submit to the Commission a request for reconsideration.

F. As soon as practicable after grading of the examination papers has been completed, every applicant will be notified in writing what his grades are. Within a period of 30 days after the notice, the applicant may request the Executive Director of the Commission for permission to review his examination papers.

G. The fee for the written examination shall be authorized as determined in Business Regulation Article, §8-302(c), Annotated Code of Maryland.

H. An applicant for a new license shall pass the examination within the 2-year period immediately preceding receipt of the license application by the Commission.

.17 Repealed.

.18 License Renewals.

A. Applications Within 2 Years of License Expiration.

(1) An application for a license previously issued which is received within 2 years from the date of the previously issued license's expiration shall be presumed to be an application for a renewal of that license.

(2) Upon a showing of good cause by the applicant, an application described in §A(1) of this regulation may be considered an application for a new license.

B. Applications After 2 Years of License Expiration.

(1) An application for a license previously issued which is received more than 2 years from the date of the previously issued license's expiration shall be presumed to be an application for a new license.

(2) Upon a showing of good cause by the applicant, an application described in §B(1), above, may be considered an application for a renewal of the previously issued license.

C. Effective Date of Renewals. A license renewed pursuant to this regulation may not be retroactive to the date that the previously issued license expired, but shall take effect on the date that the applicant fulfills the Commission's requirements for a renewal. The license shall expire 2 years from the date on which the previously issued license expired.

.19 Credit Reports.

A. An applicant for an original contractor's license shall submit to the Commission with the application a credit report from an approved credit reporting agency and a statement of all outstanding judgments against the applicant.

B. The Commission shall consider this credit report and statement in determining whether the applicant has demonstrated financial solvency as required by Business Regulation Article, § 8-311(a)(9), Annotated Code of Maryland.

.20 Interest on Guaranty Fund Repayments.

A contractor required to repay the Guaranty Fund pursuant to Business Regulation Article, § 8-410(c), Annotated Code of Maryland, shall repay the amount paid from the Fund on the contractor's account plus interest at the rate of 10 percent per annum simple interest.

.21 Television Antenna Installation.

A.   As used in this regulation, "television antenna" means a device used to receive television signals from terrestrial over-the-air-broadcasts or satellites for use in a building used or designed to be used as a residence or dwelling place of one, two, or three single family units.

B.   The installation of a television antenna may not be subject to the Maryland Home Improvement Law if all of the following criteria are met:

(1)   The party requesting the installation does not intend for the television antenna to be fabricated into and become a permanent fixed part of the building or adjacent land;

(2)   The installation does not require any substantial modification or alteration of the building to mount the television antenna or to install the wiring from the television antenna;

(3)   The attachment of the television antenna is accomplished by means of screws or other similar devices that may be removed and after removal the building does not require any repair other than repairing the screw holes and normal finishing work;

(4)   The television antenna and its attaching mount may be removed without damage to the building, the land, or the television antenna and its attaching mount; and

(5)   The installation does not require the permanent affixation of a pole or similar device to the building or adjacent land.

C.   An installation of a television antenna not meeting the criteria of § B shall be subject to the Maryland Home Improvement Law unless otherwise determined by the Commission on a case-by-case basis.

D.   A party under § C shall have the burden of persuasion that the television antenna installation is not subject to the Maryland Home Improvement Law.

.22 Outstanding Obligations.

Under Business Regulation Article, § 8-306(d)(1), Annotated Code of Maryland, an applicant's outstanding obligation is considered a financial obligation arising out of the applicant's conviction for violation of Business Regulation Article, § 8-601, Annotated Code of Maryland.

.23 Experience or Education Requirement.

A.   Trade Experience.

(1)   An applicant for a home improvement contractor's license shall have at least 2 years of trade experience.

(2)   "Trade experience" includes one or more of the following:

(a)   Participation in a registered apprenticeship program;

(b)   Employment in performing home improvements;

(c)   Employment in performing commercial or residential construction, repairs, or renovations;

(d)   Participation in a community service or charitable building or renovation program; or

(e) Performing repairs and improvements which require a building permit on one's home or the home of family members.

(3) Experience as a licensed home improvement salesperson for at least 2 years may be credited as trade experience, if the Home Improvement Commission determines that the applicant has gained substantial knowledge of the operation of a home improvement business.

B. Business Experience in Other Areas. Experience in the capacity of supervisor, manager, or owner of a business may be substituted for 1 year of the required trade experience, based on a review by the Home Improvement Commission, or an applicant for a home improvement contractor's license may substitute for the required trade experience educational training in:

(1) Vocational school training in a building trade; or

(2) Participation in a building trade work-study program.

C. Experience or educational qualifications of applicants for a home improvement contractor's license who have documented handicaps shall be considered by the Commission on an individual basis.

.24 Street Address Required.

A. This regulation applies to all applications, both original and renewal, received after April 30, 1994.

B. An applicant for a contractor license shall provide to the Commission the actual street address of the contractor's principal business office. An applicant may not provide a post office box or private mail drop as the applicant's business address of record.

.25 Arbitration Clause.

A. A mandatory arbitration clause in a home improvement contract shall include the following information:

(1) The name of the person or organization that will conduct the arbitration;

(2) Whether any mandatory fees will be charged to the parties for participation in the arbitration and include the fee schedule;

(3) Whether the arbitrator's findings are binding; and

(4) A disclosure that, under Business Regulation Article, §8-405(c), Annotated Code of Maryland, a claim against the Home Improvement Guaranty Fund by an owner shall be stayed until completion of any mandatory arbitration proceeding.

B. The parties shall affix their initials and date immediately adjacent to any mandatory arbitration clause in a home improvement contract, at the time of execution of the contract.

C. This regulation shall apply to all home improvement contracts executed after October 31, 1994.

CHAPTER 02 PROCEDURAL REGULATIONS

.01 Contested Case Hearings.

A. All contested case hearings before the Commission shall be governed by COMAR 09.01.02.

B. All contested case hearings delegated to the Office of Administrative Hearings shall be governed by COMAR 09.01.03.

CHAPTER 03 CLAIMS AGAINST THE HOME IMPROVEMENT GUARANTY FUND

.01 Scope.

This chapter shall apply to all claims arising from transactions or events occurring on or after July 1, 1988.

.02 Processing of Claims.

A. Filing of Claims. A claimant who seeks compensation from the Home Improvement Guaranty Fund ("Fund") shall file a claim with the Commission on a claim form prepared by the Commission. This claim form shall contain at a minimum:

(1) The amount claimed based on actual loss;

(2) The facts and circumstances giving rise to the claim; and

(3) An affirmation by the claimant that all statements in the claim are true.

B. Contractor's Response.

(1) The Commission shall, upon receipt of a claim, forward a copy of the claim to the contractor alleged to be responsible for the claimant's loss.

(2) A contractor to whom the Commission has forwarded a copy of a claim shall submit a written response to the allegations in the claim within 10 days of receipt of the claim.

C. Amending of Claims. Once a verified claim has been filed with the Commission, the claimant may not amend the claim unless the claimant can establish to the satisfaction of the Commission that either the:

(1) Claimant did not know and could not have reasonably ascertained the facts on which the proposed amendment is based at the time the claim was filed; or

(2) Claimant's proposed amendment would not prejudice the contractor whose conduct gave rise to the claim.

D. Review by Hearing Board.

(1) The claim, along with any written response received from a contractor, shall be referred to a hearing board of the Commission for investigation and review.

(2) Setting Claim Hearings.

(a) Unless the hearing board determines that the claim is made in bad faith, is frivolous, or is legally insufficient, the hearing board shall set the claim for a hearing before either a hearing officer, a hearing board comprised of commissioners other than the commissioners on the hearing board which reviewed the claim, or the full Commission.

(b) The hearing board may set the claim for a hearing:

(i) Solely on the claim;

(ii) On both the claim and any regulatory charges arising from the same events or transactions on which the claim was based; or

(iii) On the claim and any other outstanding claims and regulatory charges against the contractor alleged to be responsible for the claimant's loss.

(3) Dismissal of Claims by Hearing Board.

(a) Claimant's Response.

(i) If, upon initial review, the hearing board finds that the claim is frivolous, made in bad faith, or legally insufficient, the hearing board shall forward its finding, including the basis for its finding, to the claimant.

(ii) The claimant shall have 30 days from the date of the hearing board's letter forwarding its finding to respond in writing to the hearing board.

(b) Final Decision to Dismiss.

(i) If the hearing board, after a review of any written response from the claimant, determines that the claim is frivolous, made in bad faith, or legally insufficient, the hearing board shall issue an Order dismissing the claim.

(ii) Unless the Commission or any of its members determines within 15 days of the issuance by a hearing board of its Order that a full hearing by the Commission is required, the Order of the hearing board shall be a Final Order which may be appealed by the claimant directly to the circuit court where any party resides or has a principal place of business.

(c) The hearing board may dismiss a claim as legally insufficient if the claimant has unreasonably rejected good faith efforts by the contractor to resolve the claim.

(d) The hearing board may dismiss a claim as legally insufficient if the contractor was unlicensed when the contract was entered into but licensed during the performance of the contract unless:

(i) The claimant establishes by a preponderance of the evidence that the claimant did not know that the contractor was unlicensed at the time the contract was entered into; and

(ii) A substantial portion of the contractor's alleged misconduct occurred after the contractor became licensed.

E. Compulsory Binding Arbitration. When a contract between a claimant and a contractor requires that all contract disputes be submitted to binding arbitration, the claimant shall either:

(1) Submit their dispute to binding arbitration as required by the contract; or

(2) Provide evidence to the Commission that the claimant has made good faith efforts to bring the dispute to binding arbitration which the contractor has either rejected or not responded to. The Commission shall then give the contractor written notice that, if the contractor does not agree to binding arbitration, the Commission will consider the compulsory arbitration clause to be void and process the claimant's claim pursuant to this chapter.

F. Final Decisions by Court or Arbitrator. If a claimant provides the Commission with a final unappealable and non-default decision by a court or arbitrator awarding the claimant money damages against a licensed contractor when the conditions precedent to recovery set forth in Business Regulation Article, § 8-405(a) and (c), are met, the Commission shall:

(1) Send a copy of the decision to the contractor and give the contractor 21 days to comment on the decision; and

(2) Issue a Final Order to compensate the claimant from the Fund for any actual losses awarded to the claimant by the decision and not paid by the contractor, subject to the limitations set out in Regulation .03B(1) and D(2) of this chapter.

G. Time Limitation. A claim may not be brought against the Fund after 3 years from the date that the claimant discovered, or by exercise of ordinary diligence should have discovered, the loss or damage.

.03 Adjudication of Claims.

A. Claim Hearings.

(1) Parties.

(a) The claimant who brought the claim, and the contractor alleged to be responsible for the monetary loss of the claimant, shall be parties in all claim hearings.

(b) Assistant Attorneys General. Assistant attorneys general assigned to either represent the Fund on a claim, or present regulatory charges, shall participate as a party in the hearing and receive all appropriate notices.

(c) The same assistant attorney general assigned to present the regulatory case may be assigned to represent the Fund.

(2) Notice.

(a) The Commission shall notify all parties to a claim hearing of the date, time, and place of the hearing.

(b) This notice shall contain a statement of any regulatory charges brought against the contractor which will be heard at the claim hearing.

(c) The notice shall be mailed so as to give at least 10 days notice of the claim hearing.

(3) The burden of proof shall be on the claimant to establish the validity of the claim.

(4) Conduct of the Hearing.

(a) If a hearing does not involve regulatory charges, the order of presentation shall be as follows:

(i) The claimant shall present the case for the claim;

(ii) The contractor may submit any evidence against the claim;

(iii) An assistant attorney general representing the Fund may submit evidence concerning the claim; and

(iv) Any party in the hearing may cross-examine any witnesses and submit rebuttal evidence and closing arguments.

(b) If a hearing involves regulatory charges and a claim arising from the same event or transaction, the order of presentation shall be as follows:

(i)   The assistant attorney general representing the State shall present the case for the regulatory charges against the contractor;

(ii) The claimant shall present the case for the claim;

(iii) The contractor may submit evidence against the charges and the claim;

(iv) An assistant attorney general representing the Fund may submit evidence concerning the claim; and

(v)   Any party in the hearing may cross-examine any witnesses and submit rebuttal evidence and closing arguments.

(c) When a hearing involves regulatory charges and a claim arising from the same event or transaction, all evidence submitted at the hearing concerning that event or transaction shall be considered in determining the validity of the charges and the claim.

B.   Measure of Awards from Guaranty Fund.

(1) The Commission may not award from the Fund any amount for:

(a) Consequential or punitive damages;

(b) Personal injury;

(c) Attorney's fees;

(d) Court costs; or

(e) Interest.

(2) The Fund may only compensate claimants for actual losses they incurred as a result of misconduct by a licensed contractor.

(3) Unless it determines that a particular claim requires a unique measurement, the Commission shall measure actual loss as follows:

(a) If the contractor abandoned the contract without doing any work, the claimant's actual loss shall be the amount which the claimant paid to the contractor under the contract.

(b) If the contractor did work according to the contract and the claimant is not soliciting another contractor to complete the contract, the claimant's actual loss shall be the amount which the claimant paid to the original contractor less the value of any materials or services provided by the contractor.

(c) If the contractor did work according to the contract and the claimant has solicited or is soliciting another contractor to complete the contract, the claimant's actual loss shall be the amounts the claimant has paid to or on behalf of the contractor under the original contract, added to any reasonable amounts the claimant has paid or will be required to pay another contractor to repair poor work done by the original contractor under the original contract and complete the original contract, less the original contract price. If the Commission determines that the original contract price is too unrealistically low or high to provide a proper basis for measuring actual loss, the Commission may adjust its measurement accordingly.

C. Determinations.

(1) Hearing Officers.

(a) If the claim hearing is held before a hearing officer, the provisions of COMAR 09.01.03 shall be applicable.

(b) A hearing board comprised of commissioners other than commissioners who initially reviewed the claim shall adopt, reject, or modify the hearing officer's recommendations pursuant to COMAR 09.01.03.

(2) Unless the Commission or any of its members determines within 15 days of its issuance that a full hearing by the Commission is required, a hearing board's decision on a claim shall be a Final Order of the Commission which may be appealable by any aggrieved party to the circuit court where any party resides or has a principal place of business.

(3) If the claim hearing is held before the full Commission, the Commission shall issue a decision on the claim which shall be a Final Order which may be appealed by an aggrieved party to the circuit court where any party resides or has a principal place of business.

D. Payments.

(1) Upon the issuance of a Final Order that a claim is valid, with all appeals to court exhausted, the Commission shall pay the claim from the Fund subject to the limitations in § B(1) and D(2) of this regulation.

(2) The Commission may not award from the Fund:

(a) To any one claimant more than $15,000 for acts or omissions of one contractor; or

(b) More than $100,000 to claimants on account of the conduct of any one licensee, unless, after the Commission has paid out $100,000 on account of the conduct of one licensed contractor, that contractor has repaid the full $100,000.

(3) If the aggregate amount of the approved claims to be paid from the Fund involving one contractor exceeds $100,000, the Commission may either:

(a) Pay the approved claims in the order filed until the $100,000 maximum is reached; or

(b) Prorate the approved claims by awarding each claimant the same percent of their approved claim which $100,000 is of the total amount of the approved claims.

(4) For purposes of this regulation, the term "approved claim" means the amount which the Commission has approved to be paid from the Fund which cannot exceed $15,000 per claim.

SUBTITLE 01 OFFICE OF THE SECRETARY
CHAPTER 02 HEARING REGULATIONS

.01 Scope.

A. This chapter governs procedures for all contested case hearings of an administrative unit within the Department, with the exception of hearings conducted under the following:

(1) Article 48, §§167—180A, Annotated Code of Maryland, and corresponding regulations;

(2) Business Regulation Article, §3-314, Annotated Code of Maryland, and corresponding regulations;

(3) Labor and Employment Article, Title 5, Subtitle 2 and Subtitle 5, Part III, Annotated Code of Maryland, and corresponding regulations;

(4) Labor and Employment Article, Title 8, Subtitle 5, Annotated Code of Maryland, and corresponding regulations; and

(5) State Finance and Procurement Article, Title 17, Subtitle 2, Annotated Code of Maryland, and corresponding regulations.

B. The procedures in this chapter are intended to supplement the procedures required by law, and may not be construed as creating additional or contrary substantive rights.

C. An administrative unit may promulgate additional hearing regulations to supplement or modify this chapter under the administrative unit's enabling statute.

D. If a conflict exists between this chapter and the statute or regulations governing an administrative unit, the statute or regulations of the individual administrative unit shall govern.

E. If a conflict exists between this chapter and the Rules of Procedure of the Office of Administrative Hearings in COMAR 28.02.01, this chapter shall govern.

.02 Definitions.

A. In this chapter, the following terms have the meanings indicated.

B. Terms Defined.

(1) "ALJ" means an Administrative Law Judge appointed under State Government Article, §9-1604, Annotated Code of Maryland.

(2) "Administrative Procedure Act" means State Government Article, §§10-201—10-217, Annotated Code of Maryland.

(3) "Administrative unit" means a board, commission, hearing panel, committee, division, or a unit within the Department which is authorized by law or regulation to hear and determine contested cases.

(4) "Applicant" means a person seeking a new or renewal license, certificate, registration, or permit from an administrative unit.

(5) "Charging document" means a document issued by an administrative unit which sets forth:

(a) One or more violations alleged to have been committed by a respondent; or

(b) A denial or an intent to deny a license, certificate, registration, or permit.

(6) "Claim" means a claim against a guaranty fund.

(7) "Claimant" means an individual who has filed a claim against a guaranty fund.

(8) "Complaint" means a written allegation that:

(a) A licensee, registrant, certificate holder, or permit holder has committed an act which is prohibited by the appropriate statute or regulation and for which an administrative unit may take disciplinary action; or

(b) A person has practiced a regulated profession or occupation, or engaged in a business, without the required license, certificate, registration, or permit.

(9) "Contested case" has the meaning stated in the State Government Article, §10-202, Annotated Code of Maryland.

(10) "Counsel" means the attorney assigned by the Office of the Attorney General to provide a particular administrative unit with legal advice.

(11) "Department" means the Department of Labor, Licensing, and Regulation.

(12) "Final order" means the final decision of an administrative unit which contains findings of fact, conclusions of law, and a disposition which:

(a) Grants or denies a license, certificate, registration, or permit;

(b) Sanctions by reprimand, fine, suspension, or revocation;

(c) Makes a monetary award to a party from a guaranty fund or any other source, or denies an award; or

(d) Dismisses disciplinary charges.

(13) "Guaranty fund" has the meaning stated in Business Occupations and Professions Article, Title 17, Subtitle 4, Annotated Code of Maryland, and Business Regulation Article, Title 8, Subtitle 4, Annotated Code of Maryland, as applicable.

(14) "Office of Administrative Hearings" has the meaning stated in State Government Article, §9-1602, Annotated Code of Maryland.

(15) "Party" means a respondent, a claimant, an applicant, or an administrative unit, or all or some of them, as applicable.

(16) "Person" has the meaning stated in Business Regulation Article, §1-101(g), Annotated Code of Maryland.

(17) "Presenter of evidence" means the attorney assigned by the Office of the Attorney General to:

(a) Present charges and evidence against a respondent or applicant; or

(b) Represent the interests of a guaranty fund.

(18) "Presiding officer" means the chairman of an administrative unit, or in the absence of a chairman, a member of the administrative unit designated by the applicable enabling statute or by the administrative unit itself to preside over the hearing of a contested case.

(19) "Proposed decision" has the meaning stated in COMAR 28.02.01.02.

(20) "Proposed order" means the order issued by an administrative unit, after a hearing conducted by an ALJ which:

(a)   Grants or denies a license, certificate, registration, or permit;

(b)   Sanctions by reprimand, fine, suspension, or revocation;

(c)   Makes or denies a monetary award to a party from a guaranty fund or any other source; or

(d)   Dismisses the charges.

(21) "Respondent" means a person who has been called upon to answer charges made under disciplinary provisions or against whom a guaranty fund claim has been filed.

.03 Complaints.

A.   A complaint to an administrative unit may be made by any person or administrative unit.

B.   The complaint shall be in writing, and shall state the facts on which the complaint is based.

C.   In response to a complaint, an administrative unit may take one or more of the following actions:

(1)   Dismiss the complaint;

(2)   Refer the complaint for investigation;

(3)   Take appropriate informal action consistent with the facts and circumstances of the complaint;

(4)   Charge the respondent with violation of the relevant statutory and regulatory sections and give the respondent an opportunity to appear at a hearing before the administrative unit; or

(5)   Schedule a hearing before the administrative unit on a claim against a guaranty fund.

.04 Applications.

A.   An applicant who has been notified that a new or renewal license, certificate, registration, or permit, has been, or may be, denied may request a hearing before an administrative unit.

B.   The administrative unit shall hold a hearing to provide the applicant an opportunity to present evidence in support of the application.

.05 Hearing Notice.

A.   An administrative unit shall provide reasonable written notice of a hearing to the parties.

B.   The hearing notice shall contain:

(1)   The date, time, place, and nature of the hearing;

(2)   A statement of the right to present witnesses, documents, and other forms of evidence, and the right to cross-examine witnesses of another party;

(3)   A statement of the right to request subpoenas for witnesses and evidence, specifying the costs, if any, associated with the request;

(4)   The availability on request of a copy of the hearing procedure, and the costs associated with the request;

(5)   A statement of the right or restrictions pertaining to representation;

(6) A statement that failure to appear for the scheduled hearing may result in an adverse action against that party; and

(7) A statement that the parties may agree to the evidence and waive their right to appear at the hearing.

.06 Charging Document.

A.   The charging document shall be attached to the notice of hearing or incorporated in it.

B.   The charging document shall contain at least:

(1) The facts asserted, or if the facts cannot be stated in detail, the issues involved;

(2) The pertinent statutory and regulatory sections under which an administrative unit is taking action;

(3) The potential penalties; and

(4) A statement that if a hearing is not automatically scheduled, an applicant may request a hearing, and the process by which a request is made, including any time restrictions.

.07 Service of Notices, Orders, and Other Documents.

A.   Except as provided in §B of this regulation or by prior agreement of the parties, the administrative unit shall serve all notices, orders, and other documents in one of the following ways:

(1) By personal delivery;

(2) By mailing a copy of the document, first class, postage prepaid, to the person's last known business or home address; or

(3) If the person is represented by counsel, by delivering or mailing a copy of the document, first class, postage prepaid, to the person's attorney.

B.   The administrative unit shall send the hearing notice to the person against whom the action is contemplated by certified mail to the person's last known address:

(1) At least 20 days before the hearing; or

(2) If the parties have agreed to a date for which 20 days notice cannot be given, at the earliest time possible.

C.   If service of a hearing notice cannot be made under §B of this regulation, notice may be given under State Government Article, §10-209, Annotated Code of Maryland.

D.   Service under this regulation is effective on receipt.

E.   Unless the evidence shows otherwise, a document served by mail under this regulation is presumed to have been received by the addressee 3 days after the date the document was mailed.

F.   Service of a subpoena shall be made under Regulation .12 of this chapter.

.08 Representation.

A.   A party to a proceeding may:

(1) Appear in person or, if appearance by a representative is permitted by law, through a representative; or

(2) Be represented by an attorney authorized to practice in Maryland.

B.   Any notice, decision, or other matter required to be sent to a party may be sent instead to the party's attorney of record at the attorney's address, and the presumption of service in Regulation .07E of this chapter shall apply.

C.   If a party is represented by an attorney or appears through an authorized representative, all submission of evidence, examination and cross-examination of witnesses, and all objections and motions on the party's behalf shall be made solely by the attorney or the authorized representative.

.09 Failure to Appear.

A hearing may proceed as scheduled in the absence of a party if the party has:

A.   Been served in accordance with Regulation .07 of this chapter; and

B.   Failed to obtain a postponement of the hearing from the administrative unit under Regulation .10 of this chapter.

.10 Postponement.

A.   An administrative unit may postpone a hearing for good cause only if a written request for postponement is filed with the administrative unit not later than 10 days before the date of the hearing.

B.   If a request for postponement is received later than 10 days before the date of the hearing, the administrative unit shall deny the request unless it determines that there were extenuating circumstances which justified the delay.

C.   The failure of a respondent, claimant, or applicant to retain counsel or to timely request a subpoena may not be considered good cause under this regulation.

D.   A request for postponement based on failure to obtain service on a witness may not be granted if the party has failed to comply with Regulation .12 of this chapter.

.11 Discovery.

There is no prehearing discovery.

.12 Subpoenas.

A.   On request of a party to a proceeding, an administrative unit shall issue a subpoena requiring the attendance and testimony of a witness and, if requested, the production at the hearing of relevant documents and tangible items in the possession or under the control of the witness.

B.   A request for the issuance of a subpoena shall be made in writing to the administrative unit not later than 10 days before the scheduled hearing date.

C.   If a request for issuance of a subpoena is received by the administrative unit less than 15 days before the scheduled hearing date, the requesting party shall be responsible for service of the subpoena.

D.   A request for a subpoena shall specify:

(1) The full name and address of the person to be subpoenaed;

(2) The full name, address, and telephone number of the party requesting the subpoena;

(3) The caption of the action for which a subpoena is requested;

(4) The date, time, and place of the hearing for which the subpoenaed person is to appear; and

(5) For a subpoena for the production of documents, a description of tangible items, books, papers, or other documents.

E.   A subpoena request need not be served on all parties.

F.   Subpoenas may be served by:

(1) Certified mail to the person at the address specified in the subpoena request; or

(2) Personal delivery by an individual who is:

(a) 18 years old or older; and

(b) Not a party to the proceeding.

G.   Return of service of subpoena shall be made by:

(1) Affidavit, if personally delivered; or

(2) Return receipt, if mailed.

H.   A person may object to a subpoena by filing with the administrative unit, before the time specified in the subpoena for compliance, a motion to quash or for other appropriate relief.

I.   If a person fails to comply with a properly served subpoena, the party requesting the subpoena may apply to the appropriate circuit court for relief.

.13 Conduct of the Proceedings.

A.   A quorum of the administrative unit shall be present for the hearing.

B.   The presiding officer, in consultation with counsel, shall determine all procedural and evidentiary issues governed by this chapter and by the Administrative Procedure Act, and may impose reasonable time limitations.

C.   The Maryland Rules of Civil Procedure may be used as a guide in resolving procedural issues governing the conduct of the hearing that are not addressed in this chapter and the Administrative Procedure Act.

D.   The presiding officer may conduct all or any part of the hearing by telephone, television, or other electronic means, in accordance with State Government Article, §10-211, Annotated Code of Maryland.

E.   Order of Proceedings. Absent unusual circumstances, the order of proceedings in a case involving disciplinary charges against a respondent shall be as follows:

(1) Opening statements and preliminary matters may be heard;

(2) All individuals planning to testify shall be sworn before testifying;

(3) The presenter of evidence shall present the case against the respondent;

(4) The respondent or the respondent's attorney or representative may present the respondent's case;

(5) The presenter may present a rebuttal case; and

(6) The administrative unit may hear closing arguments in the same order as the presentation of evidence and may receive written memoranda of law.

F.   In a disciplinary action case which includes a claim against a guaranty fund:

(1) The claimant or the claimant's attorney shall present the claimant's case after the presenter of evidence has presented the case against the respondent;

(2) The respondent or the respondent's attorney or representative may then present the respondent's case and respond to the claim;

(3) The attorney for the guaranty fund may then present evidence on the claim; and

(4) All parties may give closing argument in the same order as the presentation of evidence.

G.   The presenter of evidence, the respondent, and the claimant may cross-examine any witness called by any party during a combined regulatory and guaranty fund hearing.

H.   In an application case the order of proceedings shall be as follows:

(1) The applicant or the applicant's attorney shall present the case in support of the application;

(2) The presenter of evidence may then present the case in opposition to the application; and

(3) The applicant may then present rebuttal.

I.   After the parties have completed their questioning of a witness, the presiding officer, members of the administrative unit, and counsel to the unit may question the witness.

J.   Upon a showing of good cause that a hearing cannot be completed on the scheduled date, an administrative unit may grant a continuance of the proceeding.

.14 Evidence.

The rules of evidence under this chapter shall be under State Government Article, §10-213, Annotated Code of Maryland.

.15 Interpreters.

A.   If a party or witness cannot readily hear, speak, or understand the spoken or written English language, and applies to the administrative unit in advance of the hearing for the appointment of a qualified interpreter to assist that party or witness, the administrative unit shall appoint a qualified interpreter to provide assistance during the hearing.

B.   With the approval of the administrative unit, a party who intends to offer the testimony of a witness who cannot readily hear, speak, or understand the spoken or written English language, may arrange for a qualified interpreter to assist the witness.

C.   An interpreter shall take an oath or affirm that the interpreter will accurately translate.

.16 Burden of Proof.

A.   In the hearing of a contested case involving allegations that the respondent violated a law or regulation, the presenter of evidence for the administrative unit shall bear the burden of proving, by a preponderance of the evidence, that the respondent committed the violations set forth in the charging document.

B.   In the hearing of a contested case resulting from the denial, or proposed denial, of a license, certificate, registration, or permit, the applicant shall have the burden of establishing, by a preponderance of the evidence, the applicant's entitlement to the license, certificate, registration, or permit.

C.   In a proceeding involving a guaranty fund claim, the claimant shall have the burden of proving, by a preponderance of the evidence, that the claimant is entitled to be compensated from the appropriate guaranty fund.

.17 Public Hearings.

Unless otherwise provided by statute, all hearings conducted under this chapter are open to the public.

.18 Recording.

A.   The administrative unit shall cause the proceedings to be recorded.

B.   The record need not be transcribed unless requested by a party or the administrative unit.

C.   The cost of a typewritten transcript of any proceeding or part of a proceeding shall be paid by the party requesting the transcript.

D.   Except as provided in §A of this regulation, cameras, tape recorders, and other electronic and photographic equipment of any type are not permitted at the hearing, unless the equipment is intended to be introduced into evidence or used to present evidence.

.19 Recusal.

A member of an administrative unit shall be recused from the review of a complaint and from participating in a hearing if the individual:

A.   Has personal knowledge of the facts which gave rise to the complaint;

B.   Has a personal or business relationship with any of the parties or witnesses; or

C.   For any other reason may be unable to act impartially in the matter.

.20 Decisions.

A.   After consideration of the testimony and other evidence, the administrative unit shall issue a written final order setting forth an appropriate disposition agreed to by a majority of the members of the unit who participated in the hearing.

B.   A member who was not present at all parts of the hearing may not vote on the disposition.

C.   The final order shall be issued within 90 days after the record of the proceeding is closed unless the administrative unit gives written notice to the parties that the time limit has been extended.

D.   The final order shall be signed by the presiding officer or a designee, and unless otherwise noted in the order, is final upon issuance.

E.   A copy of the decision shall be maintained in the files of the administrative unit.

F.   Decisions issued by an administrative unit in connection with a particular proceeding shall be mailed to the parties, or if represented by counsel to their attorney, by first-class mail within 3 business days from the date of the issuance of the order.

.21 Judicial Review.

A party aggrieved by the final decision in a contested case is entitled to judicial review of the decision under State Government Article, §10-222, Annotated Code of Maryland.

CHAPTER 03 HEARINGS DELEGATED TO THE OFFICE OF ADMINISTRATIVE HEARINGS

.01 Scope.

A.   Except as provided in §B of this regulation, this chapter governs contested case hearings that an administrative unit has delegated to the Office of Administrative Hearings for a proposed decision under State Government Article, §10-205, Annotated Code of Maryland.

B.   This chapter does not apply to cases arising under:

   (1)   Article 48, §§167—180A, Annotated Code of Maryland, and corresponding regulations;

   (2)   Business Regulation Article, §3-314, Annotated Code of Maryland, and corresponding regulations;

   (3)   Labor and Employment Article, Title 5, Subtitle 2 and Subtitle 5, Part III, Annotated Code of Maryland, and corresponding regulations;

   (4)   Labor and Employment Article, Title 8, Subtitle 5, Annotated Code of Maryland, and corresponding regulations; and

   (5)   State Finance and Procurement Article, Title 17, Subtitle 2, Annotated Code of Maryland, and corresponding regulations.

C.   If a conflict exists between this chapter and the statute or regulations governing an administrative unit, the statute or regulations of the administrative unit shall govern.

D.   If a conflict exists between this chapter and the Rules of Procedure of the Office of Administrative Hearings in COMAR 28.02.01, this chapter shall govern.

.02 Definitions.

The definitions in COMAR 09.01.02.02 apply to this chapter.

.03 Applicability.

An administrative unit, after consultation with the Office of the Attorney General, may refer contested cases to the Office of Administrative Hearings. The administrative unit shall advise the Office of Administrative Hearings of the scope of authority delegated under State Government Article, §10-205, Annotated Code of Maryland.

.04 Discovery.

There is no prehearing discovery.

.05 Proceedings.

A. Except as provided in this regulation, the ALJ shall conduct an evidentiary hearing under the Administrative Procedure Act and COMAR 28.02.01.

B. A motion to dismiss or any other dispositive motion may not be granted by the ALJ without the concurrence of all parties.

C. The presenter of evidence, the respondent, and the claimant may cross-examine any witness called by any party during a combined regulatory and guaranty fund hearing.

.06 Revocation of the Delegation of Authority.

A. For a reason specified in §B of this regulation, an administrative unit or the Department may revoke, in whole or in part, the delegation of authority to the Office of Administrative Hearings to hear a contested case at any time before the earlier of:

    (1) The issuance of a ruling on a substantive issue; or

    (2) The taking of oral testimony from the first witness.

B. The administrative unit or the Department may revoke the delegation of authority if, in the opinion of the administrative unit or the Department:

    (1) A contested case involves:

        (a) Unanticipated, novel, or unique legal or factual issues; or

        (b) Significant social, fiscal, legal, or policy issues; or

    (2) It is in the best interests of the parties to the case.

C. The administrative unit or the Department shall provide written notice of a revocation of hearing authority to all parties and the Office of Administrative Hearings.

D. The notice shall:

    (1) State the reason for the revocation of the delegation of authority; and

    (2) Specify if the revocation is in whole or in part.

E. If only a partial revocation of the delegation of authority is made, the administrative unit or the Department shall identify in the notice the portions of the contested case for which delegation of authority has been revoked.

F.   A final decision issued by the administrative unit shall reflect the fact of full or partial revocation of the delegation of authority, and a copy of the revocation notice shall be included as part of the record.

.07 Withdrawal of a Case.

A.   At any stage of the proceedings, upon the agreement of the parties, the case may be withdrawn from the Office of Administrative Hearings docket for settlement purposes.

B.   Withdrawal of the case from the Office of Administrative Hearings docket may not be deemed a dismissal of the regulatory charges or the guaranty fund claim, and may not preclude a subsequent referral to the Office of Administrative Hearings, if settlement is not accomplished.

.08 Proposed Decisions and Orders.

A.   Upon completion of the hearing, the ALJ shall submit a proposed decision to the administrative unit.

B.   The Office of Administrative Hearings may not distribute the proposed decision to the parties or to the public unless the delegation of authority specifically provides for that distribution.

C.   The proposed decision shall comply with the requirements of the Administrative Procedure Act and COMAR 28.02.01.22, and shall include:

   (1)   Written findings of fact;

   (2)   Proposed conclusions of law; and

   (3)   A recommended order.

D.   Within 60 days of receipt of the ALJ's proposed decision, an administrative unit shall:

   (1)   Review the ALJ's proposed decision;

   (2)   Issue a proposed order, which may include the ALJ's proposed decision with or without modifications; and

   (3)   Send to the parties the proposed order and a copy of the ALJ's proposed decision in the manner set forth in §G of this regulation.

E.   An administrative unit may extend the 60-day period specified in §C of this regulation by a written notice to all parties.

F.   If the proposed order changes, modifies, or amends the ALJ's proposed decision, the proposed order shall set forth an explanation of the reasons for the changes, modifications, or amendments.

G.   A proposed order shall be mailed to the parties, or to their attorneys, by first-class mail within 3 business days from the date of the issuance of the order.

H.   The proposed order or an accompanying letter shall notify the parties that they may file written exceptions with, and present arguments to, the administrative unit.

I.   If no party files timely exceptions, the proposed order of the administrative unit shall become the final order.

.09 Exceptions to the Proposed Order.

A.   Filing Exceptions.

(1)   A party adversely affected by a proposed order shall have 20 days from the postmark date of the proposed order to file exceptions with the administrative unit.

(2)   The date of filing exceptions with the administrative unit shall be the date of personal delivery to the unit or the postmark date on mailed exceptions.

B.   The exceptions may include a request that the proposed order be modified or reversed, or that the case be remanded for the taking of additional testimony.

C.   Upon receipt of exceptions to the proposed order, the administrative unit shall:

(1)   Schedule a date, time, and place for a hearing on the exceptions; and

(2)   Notify each party at least 20 days before the scheduled date of the date, time, and place of the hearing.

D.   By written request to the administrative unit, a party may waive the right to a hearing on the written exceptions.

E.   Unless a specific statute or regulation permits the hearing to be held before a panel of members of the unit, a quorum of the administrative unit shall be present at the hearing.

F.   At the hearing on exceptions, the presiding officer shall rule on all procedural issues governed by this regulation, and may impose reasonable time limitations.

G.   The record before an administrative unit on exceptions shall consist of:

(1)   The ALJ's proposed decision;

(2)   The proposed order of the administrative unit;

(3)   The exceptions filed by the parties and any responses to them;

(4)   A copy of the notice to the parties of the hearing on exceptions;

(5)   The transcript of the hearing before the ALJ, if filed with an administrative unit under §H of this regulation; and

(6)   All documentary evidence admitted into evidence before the ALJ.

H.   A party wishing to have the transcript made part of the record, shall at its own expense order the transcript and file three copies of it with the administrative unit at least 10 days before the scheduled date for the hearing on exceptions. If a transcript has already been prepared, the administrative unit shall make the transcript part of the record in the case.

I.   If the transcript has not been filed or otherwise made part of the record in the case, the parties at the hearing on exceptions may not refer to any testimony before the ALJ which was not incorporated into the ALJ's findings of fact or conclusions of law.

J.   If all parties agree, a stipulation of facts based on the record before the ALJ may be submitted instead of a transcript.

K.   Additional evidence may not be introduced unless the party seeking to introduce it demonstrates to the satisfaction of the administrative unit that the new evidence:

(1) Is relevant and material;

(2) Was not discovered before the ALJ hearing; and

(3) Could not have been discovered before the ALJ hearing with the exercise of due diligence.

L.   A party wishing to introduce additional evidence before an administrative unit at a hearing on exceptions shall file a written request at least 15 days before the scheduled date of the hearing.

.10 Final Order.

A.   The administrative unit shall issue its final order within 90 days after the date of the hearing on exceptions.

B.   The administrative unit may affirm, reverse, or modify the proposed order, or may remand the matter with specific instructions to the Office of Administrative Hearings.

C.   The administrative unit shall send a copy of the final order to the parties, or if represented by counsel to their attorneys, by first-class mail within 3 business days from the date of the issuance of the final order.

D.   The final order or an accompanying letter shall advise the parties of their rights to judicial review of the decision.

APPENDIX C
DOOR-TO-DOOR SALES ACT
Subtitle 3

§ 14-301. Definitions.

(a) In this subtitle the following words have the meanings indicated.

(b) "Business day" means any calendar day except Sunday or the following business holidays: New Year's Day, Washington's Birthday, Memorial Day, Independence Day, Labor Day, Columbus Day, Veterans' Day, Thanksgiving Day, and Christmas Day.

(c) "Consumer goods" and "consumer services" mean:

(1) Goods or services purchased, leased, or rented primarily for personal, family, or household purposes; and

(2) Courses of instruction or training regardless of the purpose for which they are taken.

(d) (1) "Door-to-door sale" means a sale, lease, or rental of consumer goods or consumer services under single or multiple contracts with a purchase price of $25 or more, in which:

(i) The seller or his representative personally solicits the sale, including a solicitation in response to or following an invitation by the buyer; and

(ii) The buyer's agreement or offer to purchase is made at a place other than the place of business of the seller.

(2) "Door-to-door sale" does not include a transaction:

(i) Made pursuant to prior negotiations in the course of a visit by the buyer to a retail business establishment which has a fixed permanent location where the consumer goods are exhibited or the consumer services are offered for sale on a continuing basis;

(ii) In which the consumer may rescind under the provisions of the federal Consumer Credit Protection Act or any regulation adopted under the Act;

(iii) In which the buyer has initiated the contact and the goods or services are needed to meet a bona fide immediate personal emergency of the buyer, and the buyer furnishes the seller with a separate dated and signed personal statement in the buyer's handwriting which describes the situation that requires immediate remedy and expressly acknowledges and waives the right to cancel the sale within three business days, and the seller in good faith makes a substantial beginning of the performance of the contract;

(iv) Conducted and consummated entirely by mail or telephone, without any other contact between the buyer and the seller or its representative before delivery of the consumer goods or performance of the consumer services;

(v) In which the buyer has initiated the contact and specifically requests the seller to visit his home to repair or perform maintenance on the buyer's personal property, except that, if, in the course of the visit, the seller sells the buyer the right to receive any additional consumer services or consumer goods, other than replacement parts necessarily used to perform the maintenance or to make the repairs, the sale of the additional consumer goods or consumer services is not within this exclusion; or

(vi) Which pertains to the sale or rental of real property, to the sale of insurance, or to the sale of securities or commodities by a broker-dealer registered with the Securities and Exchange Commission or with the Division of Securities of this State.

(e) "Person" includes an individual, corporation, business trust, estate, trust, partnership, association, two or more persons having a joint or common interest, or any other legal or commercial entity.

(f) "Place of business" means the main or permanent branch office or local address of a seller.

(g) "Purchase price" means the total price paid or to be paid for the consumer goods or consumer services, including all interest and service charges.

(h) "Sale" means a door-to-door sale.

(i) "Seller" means a person engaged in the door-to-door sale of consumer goods or consumer services.

§ 14-302. Unlawful Practices.

It is an unfair or deceptive trade practice within the meaning of Title 13 of this article for a seller to:

(1) Fail to furnish the buyer with:

(i) A fully completed receipt or copy of any contract which pertains to a door-to-door sale at the time of its execution, which is in the same language as that principally used in the oral sales presentation, shows the date of the transaction, and contains the name and address of the seller; and

(ii) A statement which is in immediate proximity to the space reserved in the contract for the signature of the buyer or, if a contract is not used, is on the front page of the receipt and which, in boldface type of a minimum size of 10 points, is in substantially the following form:

"You, the buyer, may cancel this transaction at any time prior to midnight of the third business day after the date of this transaction. See the attached notice of cancellation form for an explanation of this right.";

(2) Fail to furnish the buyer, at the time he signs the door-to-door sales contract or otherwise agrees to buy consumer goods or consumer services from the seller, a completed form in duplicate, captioned "Notice of Cancellation", which:

(i) Is attached to the contract or receipt and is easily detachable; and

(ii) Contains in 10 point boldface type the following information and statements, in the same language as that used in the contract:

"Notice of Cancellation

(Enter date of transaction)

_____
(Date)

You may cancel this transaction, without any penalty or obligation, within three business days from the above date.

If you cancel, any property traded in, any payments made by you under the contract or sale, and any negotiable instrument executed by you will be returned within 10 business days following receipt by the seller of your cancellation notice, and any security interest arising out of the transaction will be cancelled.

If you cancel, you must make available to the seller at your residence, in substantially as good condition as when received, any goods delivered to you under this contract or sale; or you may, if you wish, comply with the instructions of the seller regarding the return shipment of the goods at the seller's expense and risk.

If you do make the goods available to the seller and the seller does not pick them up within 20 days of the date of your notice of cancellation, you may retain or dispose of the goods without any further obligation. If you fail to make the goods available to the seller, or if you agree to return the goods to the seller and fail to do so, then you remain liable for performance of all obligations under the contract.

To cancel this transaction, mail or deliver a signed and dated copy of this cancellation notice or any other written notice, or send a telegram, to:

_____,   at   _____,
(name of seller)   (address of seller's place of business)

not later than midnight of _____
                                        (date)

I hereby cancel this transaction

_____   _____
(date)   (Buyer's signature)";

(3) Fail, before furnishing copies of the "Notice of Cancellation" to the buyer, to complete both copies by entering the name of the seller, the address of the seller's place of business, the date of the transaction, and the date, not earlier than the third business day following the date of the transaction, by which the buyer may give notice of cancellation;

(4) Include in any door-to-door sales contract or receipt any confession of judgment or waiver of any of the rights to which the buyer is entitled under this section, including specifically his right to cancel the sale in accordance with the provisions of this section;

(5) Fail to inform the buyer orally, at the time he signs the contract or purchases the consumer goods or consumer services, of his right to cancel;

(6) Misrepresent in any manner the buyer's right to cancel;

(7) Fail or refuse to honor any valid notice of cancellation by a buyer and, within 10 business days after the receipt of that notice, to:

(i) Refund all payments made under the contract or sale;

(ii) Return, in substantially as good condition as when received by the seller, any goods or property traded in;

(iii) Cancel and return any negotiable instrument executed by the buyer in connection with the contract or sale and take any action necessary or appropriate to terminate promptly any security interest created in the transaction;

(8) Negotiate, transfer, sell, or assign any note or other evidence of indebtedness to a finance company or other third party before midnight of the fifth business day following the day the contract was signed or the consumer goods or consumer services were purchased;

(9) Fail, within 10 business days of receiving a buyer's notice of cancellation, to notify him whether the seller intends to repossess or to abandon any shipped or delivered goods;

(10) Solicit a sale or order for sale of goods or services at the residence of a prospective buyer, without clearly, affirmatively and expressly revealing at the time the person initially contacts the prospective buyer, and before making any other statement, except a greeting, or asking the prospective buyer any other questions:

(i) The identity of the person making the solicitation.

(ii) The trade name of the person represented by the person making the solicitation.

(iii) The kind of goods or services being offered.

(iv) And, the person making the solicitation shall, in addition to meeting the requirements of paragraphs (i), (ii), and (iii), show and display identification which states the information required by paragraphs (i) and (ii) as well as the address of the place of business of one of the persons identified; or

(11) To use any plan, scheme, or ruse in soliciting a sale or order for the sale of goods or services at the residence of a prospective buyer, which misrepresents the solicitor's true status or mission for the purpose of making the sale or order for the sale of goods or services.

§ 14-303. Cancellation of sale.

If the seller violates any provision of § 14-302 of this subtitle, the buyer may cancel the door-to-door sale by notifying the seller in any manner and by any means of his intention to cancel.

§ 14-304. Civil Liability.

Any person who violates any provision of this subtitle is liable to the person affected by the violation for all damages proximately caused by the violation and for reasonable attorney fees incurred by the person damaged.

§ 14-305. Penalty.

Any person who willfully violates any provision of this subtitle is guilty of a misdemeanor and, in addition to the injunctive relief provided for in Title 13, Subtitle 4 of this article, on conviction is subject to a fine of not more than $1,000 or imprisonment of not more than one year or both.

§ 14-306. Short Title

This subtitle may be cited as the Maryland Door-to-Door Sales Act.

APPENDIX D

LIEN LAW

§ 9-101. Definitions

a) *In general.* - In this subtitle the following words have the meanings indicated.

b) *Building.* - "Building" includes any unit of a nonresidential building that is leased or separately sold as a unit.

c) *Contract.* - "Contract" means an agreement of any kind or nature, express or implied, for doing work or furnishing material, or both, for or about a building as may give rise to a lien under this subtitle.

d) *Contractor.* - "Contractor" means a person who has a contract with an owner.

(e) *Land.* - "Land" means the land to which a lien extends under this subtitle or the land within the boundaries established by proceedings in accordance with the Maryland Rules. "Land" includes the improvements to the land.

(f) *Owner.* - "Owner" means the owner of the land except that, when the contractor executes the contract with a tenant for life or for years, "owner" means the tenant.

(g) *Subcontractor.* - "Subcontractor" means a person who has a contract with anyone except the owner or his agent.

§ 9-102. Property subject to lien.

(a) *Buildings.* - Every building erected and every building repaired, rebuilt, or improved to the extent of 15 percent of its value is subject to establishment of a lien in accordance with this subtitle for the payment of all debts, without regard to the amount, contracted for work done for or about the building and for materials furnished for or about the building, including the drilling and installation of wells to supply water, the construction or installation of any swimming pool or fencing, the sodding, seeding or planting in or about the premises of any shrubs, trees, plants, flowers or nursery products, the grading, filling, landscaping, and paving of the premises, and the leasing of equipment, with or without an operator, for use for or about the building or premises.

(b) *Waterlines, sewers, drains and streets in development.* - If the owner of land or the owner's agent contracts for the installation of waterlines, sanitary sewers, storm drains, or streets to service all lots in a development of the owner's land, each lot and its improvements, if any, are subject, on a basis pro rata to the number of lots being developed, to the establishment of a lien as provided in subsection (a) of this section for all debts for work and material in connection with the installation.

(c) *Machines, wharves, and bridges.* - Any machine, wharf, or bridge erected, constructed, or repaired within the State may be subjected to a lien in the same manner as a building is subjected to a lien in accordance with this subtitle.

(d) *Exemptions* - However, a building or the land on which the building is erected may not be subjected to a lien under this subtitle if, prior to the establishment of a lien in accordance with this subtitle, legal title has been granted to a bona fide purchaser for value.

(e) *Filing of petition constitutes notice to purchaser* - The filing of a petition under § 9-105 shall constitute notice to a purchaser of the possibility of a lien being perfected under this subtitle.

§ 9-103. Extent of lien

(a) A lien established in accordance with this subtitle shall extend to the land covered by the building and to as much other land, immediately adjacent and belonging in like manner to the owner of the building, as may be necessary for the ordinary and useful purposes of the building. The quantity and boundaries of the land may be designated as provided in this section.

(b) An owner of any land who desires to erect any building or to contract with any person for its erection may define, in writing, the boundaries of the land appurtenant to the building before the commencement of construction, and then file the boundaries for record with the clerk of the circuit court for the county. The designation of boundaries shall be binding on all persons. If the boundaries are not designated before the commencement of a building, the owner of the land or any person having a lien or encumbrance on the land by mortgage, judgment, or otherwise entitled to establish a lien in accordance with this subtitle may apply, by written petition, to the circuit court for the county to designate the boundaries.

(c) (1) If a building is commenced and not finished, a lien established in accordance with this subtitle shall attach to the extent of the work done or material furnished.

(2) If a building is erected, or repaired, rebuilt or improved to the extent of 25 percent of its value, by a tenant for life or years or by a person employed by the tenant, any lien established in accordance with this subtitle applies only to the extent of the tenant's interest.

§ 9-104. Notice to owner by subcontractor.

(a) *Notice required to entitle subcontractor to lien -*

(1) A subcontractor doing work or furnishing materials or both for or about a building other than a single family dwelling being erected on the owner's land for his own residence is not entitled to a lien under this subtitle unless, within 120 days after doing the work or furnishing the materials, the subcontractor gives written notice of an intention to claim a lien substantially in the form specified in subsection (b) of this section.

(2) A subcontractor doing work or furnishing materials or both for or about a single family dwelling being erected on the owner's land for his own residence is not entitled to a lien under this subtitle unless, within 120 days after doing work or furnishing materials for or about that single family dwelling, the subcontractor gives written notice of an intention to claim a lien in accordance with subsection (a)(1) of this section and the owner has not made full payment to the contractor prior to receiving the notice.

(b) *Form of notice.* - The form of notice is sufficient for the purposes of this subtitle if it contains the information required and is substantially in the following form:

"Notice to Owner or Owner's Agent of Intention to Claim a Lien

_____

(Subcontractor)

did work or furnished material for or about the building generally designated or briefly described
as

_____

_____

The total amount earned under the subcontractor's undertaking to the date hereof is $ _____
of which $ _____ is due and unpaid as of the date hereof. The work done or materials
provided under the subcontract were as follows: (insert brief description of the work done and
materials furnished, the time when the work was done or the materials furnished, and the name
of the person for whom the work was done or to whom the materials were furnished).

I do solemnly declare and affirm under the penalties of perjury that the contents of the foregoing
notice are true to the best of the affiant's knowledge, information, and belief.

_____

(Individual)

on behalf of _____

(Subcontractor)

(Insert if subcontractor is not an individual)"

(c) *Notice by mail or personal delivery.* - The notice is effective if given by registered or
certified mail, return receipt requested, or personally delivered to the owner by the claimant or
his agent.

(d) *More than one owner.* - If there is more than one owner, the subcontractor may comply with
this section by giving the notice to any of the owners.

(e) *Notice by posting.* - If notice cannot be given on account of absence or other causes, the
subcontractor, or his agent, in the presence of a competent witness and within 120 days, may
place the notice on the door or other front part of the building. Notice by posting according to
this subsection is sufficient in all cases where the owner of the property has died and his
successors in title do not appear on the public records of the county.

(f) *Payments by owner to contractor after notice; limitation on lien against certain single family
dwellings.* -

(1) On receipt of notice given under this section, the owner may withhold, from sums due the
contractor, the amount the owner ascertains to be due the subcontractor giving the notice.

(2) If the subcontractor giving notice establishes a lien in accordance with this subtitle, the
contractor shall receive only the difference between the amount due him and that due the
subcontractor giving the notice.

(3) Notwithstanding any other provision of this section to the contrary, the lien of the subcontractor against a single family dwelling being erected on the land of the owner for his own residence shall not exceed the amount by which the owner is indebted under the contract at the time the notice is given.

§ 9-105. Filing of claims.

(a) In order to establish a lien under this subtitle, a person entitled to a lien shall file proceedings in the circuit court for the county where the land or any part of the land is located within 180 days after the work has been finished or the materials furnished. The proceedings shall be commenced by filing with the clerk, the following:

(1) A petition to establish the mechanic's lien, which shall set forth at least the following:

(i)   The name and address of the petitioner;

(ii)   The name and address of the owner;

(iii) The nature or kind of work done or the kind and amount of materials furnished, the time when the work was done or the materials furnished, the name of the person for whom the work was done or to whom the materials were furnished and the amount or sum claimed to be due, less any credit recognized by the petitioner;

(iv) A description of the land, including a statement whether part of the land is located in another county, and a description adequate to identify the building; and

(v) If the petitioner is a subcontractor, facts showing that the notice required under § 9-104 of this subtitle was properly mailed or served upon the owner, or, if so authorized, posted on the building. If the lien is sought to be established against two or more buildings on separate lots or parcels of land owned by the same person, the lien will be postponed to other mechanics' liens unless the petitioner designates the amount he claims is due him on each building;

(2) An affidavit by the petitioner or some person on his behalf, setting forth facts upon which the petitioner claims he is entitled to the lien in the amount specified; and

(3) Either original or sworn, certified or photostatic copies of material papers or parts thereof, if any, which constitute the basis of the lien claim, unless the absence thereof is explained in the affidavit.

(b) The clerk shall docket the proceedings as an action in equity, and all process shall issue out of and all pleadings shall be filed in the one action.

§ 9-106. Procedure following filing of claim.

(a) *Review of pleadings and documents filed; order to show cause; opposing affidavit; answer showing cause. -*

(1) When a petition to establish a mechanic's lien is filed, the court shall review the pleadings and documents on file and may require the petitioner to supplement or explain any of the matters therein set forth. If the court determines that the lien should attach, it shall pass an order that directs the owner to show cause within 15 days from the date of service on the owner of a copy

of the order, together with copies of the pleadings and documents on file, why a lien upon the land or building and for the amount described in the petition should not attach. Additionally, the order shall inform the owner that:

(i) He may appear at the time stated in the order and present evidence in his behalf or may file a counteraffidavit at or before that time; and

(ii) If he fails to appear and present evidence or file a counteraffidavit, the facts in the affidavit supporting the petitioner's claim shall be deemed admitted and a lien may attach to the land or buildings described in the petition.

(2) If the owner desires to controvert any statement of fact contained in the affidavit supporting the petitioner's claim, he must file an affidavit in support of his answer showing cause. The failure to file such opposing affidavit shall constitute an admission for the purposes of the proceedings of all statements of fact in the affidavit supporting the petitioner's claim, but shall not constitute an admission that such petition or affidavit in support thereof is legally sufficient.

(3) An answer showing cause why a lien should not be established in the amount claimed shall be set down for hearing at the earliest possible time.

(b) *Final order; interlocutory order.* -

(1) If the pleadings, affidavits and admissions on file, and the evidence, if any, show that there is no genuine dispute as to any material fact and that the lien should attach as a matter of law, then a final order shall be entered establishing the lien for want of any cause shown to the contrary. Further, if it appears that there is no genuine dispute as to any portion of the lien claim, then the validity of that portion shall be established and the action shall proceed only on the disputed amount of the lien claim.

(2) If the pleadings, affidavits and admissions on file and the evidence, if any, show that there is no genuine dispute as to any material fact and that the petitioner failed to establish his right to a lien as a matter of law, then a final order shall be entered denying the lien for cause shown.

(3) If the court determines from the pleadings, affidavits and admissions on file, and the evidence, if any, that the lien should not attach, or should not attach in the amount claimed, as a matter of law, by any final order, but that there is probable cause to believe the petitioner is entitled to a lien, the court shall enter an interlocutory order which:

(i)   Establishes the lien;

(ii) Describes the boundaries of the land and the buildings to which the lien attaches;

(iii) States the amount of the claim for which probable cause is found;

(iv) Specifies the amount of a bond that the owner may file to have the land and building released from the lien;

(v)   May require the claimant to file a bond in an amount that the court believes sufficient for damages, including reasonable attorney's fees; and (vi)Assigns a date for the trial of all the matters at issue in the action, which shall be within a period of six months. The owner or any other person interested in the property, however, may, at any time, move to have the lien established by the interlocutory order modified or dissolved.

(c) The amount of and the surety on any bond shall be determined and approved pursuant to the Maryland Rules except as set forth in this subtitle. The petitioner, or any other person interested in the property, however, if not satisfied with the sufficiency of a surety or with the amount of any bond given, may, at any time before entry of a final decree, apply to the court for an order requiring an additional bond, and upon notice to the other parties involved, the court may order the giving of such additional bond as it may deem proper. In lieu of filing bond, any party may deposit money in an amount equal to the amount of the bond which would otherwise be required, pursuant to the Maryland Rules.

(d) Until a final order is entered either establishing or denying the lien, the action shall proceed to trial on all matters at issue, as in the case of any other proceedings in equity.

§ 9-107. Attachment of lien to land in another county.

(a) If any part of the land is located within another county and the petitioner desires that the lien attach to the land in that county, the petitioner shall file a certified copy of the docket entries, of the court order, and of any required bond with the clerk of the circuit court for that county.

(b) A lien attaches to the land or building in a county as of the time the documents required to be filed under subsection (a) of this section are filed with the clerk of the circuit court of that county.

§ 9-108. Sale under forecloure or execution of land against which lien is established.

If all or any part of the land or buildings against which a mechanic's lien has been established pursuant to this subtitle shall be sold under foreclosure or a judgment, execution or any other court order, all liens and encumbrances on such property shall be satisfied in accordance with their priority, subject to the limitation in the next sentence of this section. If the proceeds of the sale are insufficient to satisfy all liens established pursuant to this subtitle, then all proceeds available to satisfy each such lien shall be stated by the court auditor as one fund, and the amount to be disbursed to satisfy each lien established pursuant to this subtitle shall bear the same proportion to that fund as the amount of such lien bears to the total amount secured by all such liens, without regard to priority among such liens.

§ 9-109.

The right to enforce any lien established under this subtitle expires at the end of one year from the day on which the petition to establish the lien was first filed. During this time the claimant may file a petition in the lien proceedings to enforce the lien or execute on any bond given to obtain a release of the land and building from the lien. If such petition is filed within the one-year period, the right to a lien or the lien, or any bond given to obtain a release of lien, shall remain in full force and effect until the conclusion of the enforcement proceedings and thereafter only in accordance with the decree entered in the case.

§ 9-110.

No person having the right to establish a mechanics' lien waives the right by granting a credit, or receiving a note or other security, unless it is received as payment or the lien right is expressly waived.

§ 9-111.

Nothing in this subtitle affects the right of any person, to whom any debt is due for work done or material furnished, to maintain any personal action against the owner of the building or any other person liable for the debt.

§ 9-112.

This law is remedial and shall be so construed to give effect to its purpose. Any amendment shall be made in the proceedings, commencing with the claim or lien to be filed and extending to all subsequent proceedings, as may be necessary and proper. However, the amount of the claim or lien filed may not be enlarged by amendment.

§ 9-113.

(a) An executory contract between a contractor and any subcontractor that is related to construction, alteration, or repair of a building, structure, or improvement may not waive or require the subcontractor to waive the right to:

(1) Claim a mechanics' lien; or

(2) Sue on a contractor's bond.

(b) A provision in an executory contract between a contractor and a subcontractor that is related to construction, alteration, or repair of a building, structure, or improvement and that conditions payment to the subcontractor on receipt by the contractor of payment from the owner or any other third party may not abrogate or waive the right of the subcontractor to:

(1) Claim a mechanics' lien; or

(2) Sue on a contractor's bond.

(c) Any provision of a contract made in violation of this section is void as against the public policy of this State.

§ 9-114.

(a) At the time of settlement or payment in full between a contractor and an owner, the contractor shall give to the owner a signed release of lien from each material supplier and subcontractor who provided work or materials under the contract.

(b) An owner is not subject to a lien and is not otherwise liable for any work or materials included in the release under subsection (a) of this section.

APPENDIX E

EXCERPTS FROM
AMERICANS WITH DISABILITES ACT
REQUIREMENTS FACT SHEET

U.S. Department of Justice
Civil Rights Division
Coordination and Review Section
CRD-20
GPO : 1990 0 - 273-184

EMPLOYMENT

Employers may not discriminate against an individual with a disability in hiring or promotion if the person is otherwise qualified for the job.

Employers can ask about one's ability to perform a job, but cannot inquire if someone has a disability or subject a person to tests that tend to screen out people with disabilities.

Employers will need to provide "reasonable accommodation" to individuals with disabilities. This includes steps such as job restructuring and modification of equipment.

Employers do not need to provide accommodations that impose "undue hardship" on business operations.

Who needs to comply:

All employers with 25 or more employees must comply, effective July 26, 1992.

All employers with 15-24 employees must comply, effective July 26, 1994.

APPENDIX F

REFERENCES FOR FURTHER STUDY

CHAPTER 4
Estimating

ESTIMATING FOR CONTRACTORS: HOW TO MAKE ESTIMATES THAT WIN JOBS, Cook, 1982, R.S. Means Company

ESTIMATING & BIDDING FOR BUILDERS & REMODELERS, Langedyk, 1996 Craftsman Book Company

ESTIMATING FOR HOME BUILDERS, Householder & Mouton, 1992, Home Builder Press

COST RECORDS FOR CONSTRUCTION ESTIMATING, Jackson, 1998, Craftsman Book Co.

COMPUTER ESTIMATING FOR HOME BUILDERS, 1998, HAHB & Home Builder Press

ESTIMATING IN BUILDING CONSTRUCTION, 5th Edition, Dagostino & Feigenbaum, Prentice Hall

CHAPTER 5
Scheduling

REAL WORLD CONSTRUCTION SCHEDULING, Coombes, 1990, Construction Planning & Management, Inc.

SCHEDULING FOR BUILDERS, 2nd Edition, Householder, 1990, Home Builder Press

CPM CONSTRUCTION SCHEDULER'S MANUAL, Hutchings, 1995, McGraw Hill

MEANS SCHEDULING MANUAL, 3rd Edition, Horskey, 1991, R. S. Means Co.

BAR CHART SCHEDULING FOR RESIDENTIAL CONSTRUCTION, Love, 1998, Home Builder Press

SCHEDULING RESIDENTIAL CONSTRUCTION FOR BUILDERS AND REMODELERS, Love, 1995, Home Builder Press

CHAPTER 6
Safety

FR 29 Part 1926 **OSHA SAFETY AND HEALTH STANDARDS FOR THE CONSTRUCTION INDUSTRY**

OTHER OSHA PUBLICATIONS:

#2056	ALL ABOUT OSHA
#2098	OSHA INSPECTIONS
#3021	EMPLOYEE WORKPLACE RIGHTS
#3047	CONSULTATION SERVICES FOR THE EMPLOYER
#3071	JOB HAZARD ANALYSIS
#3077	PERSONAL PROTECTIVE EQUIPMENT
#3079	RESPIRATORY PROTECTION
#3084	CHEMICAL HAZARD COMMUNICATION
#3088	HOW TO PREPARE FOR WORKPLACE EMERGENCIES
#3096	ASBESTOS STANDARDS FOR THE CONSTRUCTION INDUSTRY
#3110	ACCESS TO MEDICAL AND EXPOSURE RECORDS

AN OUNCE OF PREVENTION: JOBSITE SAFETY & INSURANCE FOR BUILDERS & REMODELERS, Story, 1995

OSHA MADE EASY: A GUIDE TO RECORD KEEPING, REPORTING & COMPLIANCE, Moran & Moran, 1994

CHAPTER 7
Employer
Obligations

HANDY REFERENCE GUIDE TO THE FAIR LABOR STANDARDS ACT, Wage & Hour Publication # 1282, U.S. Department of Labor, Wage & Hour Division

CIRCULAR E, EMPLOYER'S TAX GUIDE, Publication 15, January 2005 Department of Treasury, Internal Revenue Service

ADA–YOUR RESPONSIBILITIES AS AN EMPLOYER, Publication #EEOC-BK-17, U.S. Equal Employment Opportunities Commission

FAMILY MEDICAL LEAVE ACT OF 1993, Wage & Hour Publication #1419, 1995, U.S. Department of Labor, Wage & Hour Division

CFR 8 PARTS 214 & 274A IMMIGRATION AND NATURALIZATION SERVICE, 1991, INS Publication #1403-91

CHAPTER 8
Finance

BUILDER'S GUIDE TO ACCOUNTING, Thomsett, 2001, Craftsman Book Company

ACCOUNTING AND FINANCIAL MANAGEMENT FOR BUILDERS, REMODELERS AND DEVELOPERS, 3rd Edition, 1993, Home Builder Press

CONSTRUCTION ACCOUNTING, Adrain, 1993, Stripes Publishing

CONTRACTORS GUIDE TO QUICKBOOKS PRO 2003, Mitchell, Savage, and Erwin, 2003, Craftsman Book Company

QUICKEN FOR CONTRACTORS, Mitchell, Erwin, Savage and Underwood 1998, Craftsman Book Company

CONSTRUCTION CONTRACTORS – AUDIT AND ACCOUNTING GUIDE, AICPA, 1997, CCH Incorporated

CHAPTER 9
Contract Law

CONSTRUCTION FORMS & CONTRACTS, Savage & Jones – Mitchell, 1994, Craftsman Book Company

AVOIDING OR MINIMIZING CONSTRUCTION LITIGATION, Jonathon J. Sweet, 1993, John Wiley & Sons